Sir Henry Fowler

A Versatile Life

The biography of Sir Henry Fowler, KBE, LLD, JP

by
John Chacksfield
FBIS, MRAeS, AFAIAA, C. Eng

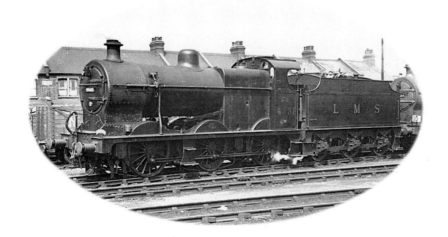

THE OAKWOOD PRESS

© Oakwood Press & John Chacksfield 2000

British Library Cataloguing in Publication Data
A Record for this book is available from the British Library
ISBN 0 85361 550 0

Typeset by Oakwood Graphics.
Repro by Ford Graphics, Ringwood, Hants.
Printed by Oakdale Printing Company Ltd., Poole, Dorset.

To my wife, who patiently tolerated my immersion in matters surrounding this book for the year of research associated with its preparation.

The 'Baby Scots' were capable of much that a 'Royal Scot' could do. Here No. 5905 heads a down express, at least 14, past Elstree. *R.S. Carpenter Collection*

Title page: Despite its drawbacks the '4F' continued in production. This being built at Crewe in 1928 is found at Shoeburyness in 1936. *H.F. Wheeller Collection*
Front cover, top: Charcoal sketch of Sir Henry Fowler *c.* 1928-9 *Mrs D. Fowler*
Front cover, bottom: A contemporary commercial postcard of Sir Henry Fowler's *Royal Scot.* *John Alsop Collection*

Published by The Oakwood Press (Usk), P.O. Box 13, Usk, Mon., NP15 1YS.

E-Mail: oakwood-press@dial.pipex.com
Website: http://ds.dial.pipex.com/oakwood-press

Contents

> 'If you will let me, I will wish you in your future what all men desire - enough work to do, and strength enough to do your work.'
>
> *Rudyard Kipling*
>
> *Taken from Lady Emma Fowler's diary for 1932*

Sir Henry Fowler, a photographic portrait *c.* 1928.   *Crown Copyright*

Foreword

If a prize had been offered in the mid-1920s for the best known and most likeable Chief Mechanical Engineer (CME) of the four recently grouped railways, it would have been won hands down by Sir Henry Fowler. In addition to his work for the largest railway, usually referred to at that time as the 'L M 'n S', he had extensive interests in sport and in local activities around his home at Spondon, near Derby. He was also in constant demand as President or other high rank by most of the Engineering Institutions. Remarkably, he maintained these wide-ranging interests from the early 1900s until his retirement in 1932.

Strangely, his most important achievements were not directly concerned with his railway - though that in no way detracts from his value as a Railway Biography subject.

His knighthood was earned by outstanding war effort, first as Director of Production for all munitions work throughout the country; and later, from early 1918, as Deputy Director of Aircraft Production which included his relaunch of the Royal Aircraft Establishment, Farnborough.

His international prestige was enhanced by membership of the governing body of the International Railway Congress Association.

Why, then, one might ask, should these achievements eclipse his job as CME? I think the answer lies in his early days on the Lancashire & Yorkshire Railway (L&YR) under Aspinall. He was the brainiest of the Horwich quartet which included Hughes, Maunsell and Gresley. He won a Whitworth Exhibition in 1891 at age 20 and was put in the Test Room while still an apprentice. He soon became its Manager, then added the Gas Department; and performed so well that Derby took him as Research and Gas Manager in 1900. By 1907 he was Works Manager, and as the year 1910 opened he was CME of the Midland Railway.

That sounds grand, but there was a flaw which turned out to be serious: he had spent no time in the Drawing Office, nor on any locomotive design work, and he had no running shed or footplate experience. These empty spaces, coupled with his very sympathetic but hearty approach to discussions, explain why he tolerated three separate LMS drawing offices, all mutually antagonistic!

He should have integrated them into a forward-looking team - and he had the data to set their goal-posts from the 2-6-0 and 2-8-0 criteria set out by the Association of Railway Locomotive Engineers in 1918. His biographer finds fair excuses for this failure, which left the LMS floundering with small engines until he adroitly borrowed 'Lord Nelson' drawings from Maunsell in 1927 and got the North British Locomotive Company to design the 'Royal Scot'. But there was no follow-up of new locomotive design and he wisely switched to full time work on establishing the new LMS Research Department (and on his other wide interests) to make way for Stanier to be the CME in 1932. This slightly clouded his last four years with the LMS, as some blamed him for the 'greatwesternisation' of Derby; but his 1932-33 letters from Cairo retain all the usual Fowler nonchalance.

Sir Henry never took personal credit for engines, not even the 'Royal Scot'. He certainly would have credited others for all the achievements in Appendix Three. I expect he took the blame, if any, for the zero achievement of Appendix Six.

H.A.V. Bulleid
24th August, 1999

5

Preamble

'My worst enemy is time'. **Sir Henry Fowler**

Maybe this explains Henry Fowler's propensity to work, play and be involved in extraneous business all at a high rate. It was as though he felt that life itself was moving at a high speed and, to keep up with events, he needed to get things done quickly. This attitude permeated through to his staff, in that he expected them to match his own speed. Perhaps this was one reason why it was difficult to impress on him the need to take a careful look at specific design features of benefit to locomotive performance and economy. He simply could not find the time to absorb the precepts being put forward, for it was clear that his workload, in the 1914-18 War and the 1920s in particular, was incredibly high. Many an engineer would have cracked under the strain. Being a heavily-built, energetic, person the effort involved in keeping to his normal fast-paced approach to work was considerable and must eventually have taken its toll on his health, which gradually began to fail in his mid- to late-sixties.

A good delegator and brilliant organiser, Fowler was a personable, likeable and, on the whole, pleasant man. He could converse with people in all walks of life, having the knack of putting them at ease from the first few words. From the man on the shop floor to the King, he could encourage the flow of relaxed conversation. In a social context, his cheerful and often thoughtful manner won many friends and admirers in the towns where he lived. Above all, his sincere Christian beliefs were ever present in his life, both at work and at home. Every letter he wrote to his wife Emma, whom he adored, ended by wishing God's blessing upon her and their family.

A much criticised engineer, Sir Henry Fowler was an admirable person who carried out his tasks speedily and efficiently, and it is to be hoped that this biography will put fully into perspective his great achievements against the background of sometimes flawed management decisions outside of his control. He most certainly did as he was requested and began the transformation of the motive power spectrum of the largest railway of the Grouping of 1923, once he had taken the CME's position upon George Hughes' retirement in 1925.

Versatility was one of his many attributes, there was not much, in an engineering context, that he could not put his hand to.

A line-up outside the paint shop at Derby works, September 1925. *R.S. Carpenter Collection*

Introduction and Acknowledgements

Much has been written about Henry Fowler and the small engine policy which was, for so long, a Derby trait. Unfortunately many of those writings have delved into the background of managerial decisions rather than how Fowler dealt with the immediate task of providing motive power as specified by those in power and with the ears of the Boardroom. Their policies may have been guided by personal fancies and technical constraints and, in some cases, were most certainly flawed. However, in his interpretation of their needs Henry Fowler most definitely came up with the goods specified and satisfied their requirements. If he had not, he would have been removed from office.

As the Midland Railway (MR) was absorbed into the large London, Midland and Scottish Railway (LMS) at Grouping, Derby was able to retain its ascendancy in the locomotive sphere despite the appointment of George Hughes of the Lancashire and Yorkshire Railway (L&YR) as Chief Mechanical Engineer. Hughes made the classic error of remaining at Horwich for his short term of office for the LMS and thus Derby was, under Fowler, in a position to put itself forward as the leader once Hughes had retired.

Although, after Grouping, the small engine policy of the former MR was starting to be eroded by the LMS requirements, and Henry Fowler had, in fact, commenced the introduction of new six-coupled passenger and eight-coupled freight locomotives, considerable emphasis on smaller four-coupled types continued to be put forward. By the end of the 1920s, it was clear to the top management, by now changed quite considerably from the MR-dominated team of 1923, that a clean sweep of design matters was needed, with the emphasis placed on replacing many of the by now outdated locomotives of the LNWR, L&YR, MR and other parties to the grouping. Only a few of these were from the latest school of design thinking. To be fair to Fowler, in respect of some of the LMS designs attributed to him, he had accepted the inevitability of the long-lap, long travel valve gear concept and not opposed the employment of it on some of them. He had also long been an exponent of superheating and good boiler design.

The few years attributed to Fowler (Sir Henry, as he was then) as CME of the largest Grouping conglomerate were years in which many thousands of new locomotives were produced, using the four major LMS plants as well as some nine different private builders. His grasp of the organisational needs in seeing that this was achieved on schedule pointed to a flair for the management of complex matters rarely seen except in the most capable of production engineers. He achieved much for the early LMS and laid the foundation for his successor, Stanier, to build upon in the massive programme of restocking the railway with modern and efficient locomotives, some of which were derivatives of the best of Fowler's, which was the task in the 1930s and 1940s.

Some may not also realise that Fowler was recognised as a competent organiser and delegator who was called into Government service during World War I with the Ministry of Munitions, which eventually sent him to oversee the Royal Aircraft Factory at Farnborough followed by time as Deputy Director-General of Aircraft Production in 1918. This part of his career is covered in some detail owing to the important part it played in equipping the RFC with new fighters. It also produced the well-deserved knighthood.

I must acknowledge here the considerable help from many sources that produced information to complete this biography. Top of the list must be Mrs Dorothy Fowler, widow of Eric Fowler, Sir Henry's youngest son. Without her generous supply of family archives, including Sir Henry's letters and photographs plus Lady Emma Fowler's diaries, the personal information would have been very sparse. Much information on the Fowler's time in Spondon came from John Hughes of the Spondon Historical Society and Miss Joyce Wright, whose father was one of Henry Fowler's Bible Class members. She had, in addition to some photographs, several letters written by Henry carefully preserved and gladly loaned them to me to aid in my research. The *Derby Telegraph*, through its library, also provided much data from the comprehensive archives it holds. The Derby Local Studies Library enabled electoral records to be studied which traced some of the Fowlers' moves around the city, in addition to much local information of interest. A special thanks also to the late Eric Langridge, who despite being in his 103rd year, freely corresponded with information on the Locomotive Drawing Office under Fowler and Hughes, some of that being in Midland Railway days. Both the Defence Evaluation and Research Agency (DERA) archives at Pyestock and the Royal Aeronautical Society (RAeS) Library provided much information on Fowler's time as Superintendent at Farnborough and the Royal Flying Corps aircraft of the time. The NRM again was a source of much useful data, via Philip Atkins in the Library. Additionally, as always happens in my railway publications, George Carpenter's weekly gathering at the Institute of Civil Engineers has brought to my notice several facts and figures concerning the Fowler days, notably involving James Anderson. Thank you, George. The illustrations of the Northern Counties Committee locomotives came from Jim Jarvis, and on the other locomotive photos a special vote of thanks are due to John Scott-Morgan for opening up his collection of archive negatives and also for arranging that the Roger Carpenter collection be made available. Finally, I must state my appreciation for Anthony Bulleid's Foreword and his thorough reading of my draft text to check it for accuracy with regard to happenings at Derby Works, where he was an apprentice in the early 1930s.

Here, then, is the story of how Henry Fowler reached the top of his profession and left his mark upon the locomotive side of a major British railway and many engineering institutions.

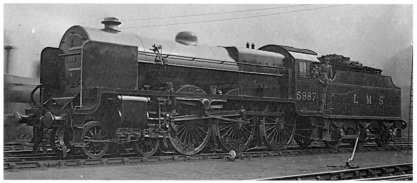

'Patriot' No. 5987 at Crewe North 1933.   *A.W.V. Mace Collection*

Chapter One

The Early Days

For at least nine generations of the Fowlers the Christian name Henry crops up. Large numbers of this family were to adopt the Quaker faith, although in about 1820-40 some of them were to return to the Church of England. However, the strict teachings and habits of the Society of Friends imbued the family with a strong Christian faith which passed down through the years.

The first Henry Fowler is recorded as having been born around 1610, the first son of Richard Fowler himself the younger son of Thomas Fowler, who lived at Stretton-on-the-Fosse, Warwickshire. This Henry Fowler, together with three of his four brothers, Stephen, Thomas, Christopher and Richard, was apprenticed to silk weavers in London. Following his apprenticeship Henry returned to the area of his birth and set up a silk weaving business and shop at Evesham around 1640. He settled down and married and had four children: Henry, John, Mary and Margaret. These four children were all to become Quakers, as had their father, and this was to become the religious belief of this branch of the Fowlers for nearly two centuries. The eldest son, Henry, followed in his father's footsteps, becoming a silk weaver and taking over the family busines in Evesham.

In 1803 the Fowlers were still established in Evesham and a further Henry was born this year. He carried on in the trade for so long established, branching out into general upholstery and furnishings, and on 25th August, 1836, married Elizabeth Hawkes at St Peter's, Bengeworth, Evesham. Clearly, at some time prior to this, the Fowlers of this line had reverted to the Church of England.

Henry and Elizabeth had eight children, Elizabeth (b.1837), Sarah (b.1838), George (b.1840), Winifred (b.1841), Henry (b.1843), Jane (b.1845), Susan (b.1847) and Ann (b.1849). George only lived four months, but the rest of the family were to live into the 20th century. The surviving son, Henry, after a childhood spent at Upton-on-Severn and Pershore, settled back at Evesham to take over his father's business, classing himself as an upholsteror. In 1869, he married his Welsh sweetheart Mary Hughes and settled down into married life and the normal run of producing a family. His forbears, being Quakers, had produced in him a strict approach to family life. Henry and Mary were to have seven children over the years, all to be brought up in a firm, but fair, environment engendered by Henry's background. He is recorded as being quite a martinet.

The first of these seven children, a son, was born on the 29th July, 1870 and was named Henry, after his father, and is the subject of this narrative. His childhood, and that of his three brothers, Alex, Arthur and Charles and three sisters, Jeanie, Bessie and Mollie, was permeated with many outdoor pursuits which undoubtedly lead to his future sporting involvements. The river Avon, which flowed nearby was used for rowing exercises and, on Christmas morning in particular, the Fowler menfolk were to be found having a bracing swim! Life was certainly hard and young Henry, throughout his life, was to be noted for an industrious approach to all in which he was involved. Most certainly his early childhood experiences had encouraged this trait, as they also did for his involvement in sports of many and varied kinds. He worked hard and played hard.

Henry Fowler, Sir Henry's grandfather.   *Mrs D. Fowler*

Elizabeth Fowler (née Hawkes), Sir Henry's grandmother.   *Mrs D. Fowler*

Mary Hughes, Sir Henry's mother, before her marriage to Henry Fowler Snr.   *Mrs D. Fowler*

Henry Fowler at about one year old.
Mrs D. Fowler

A rather faded photograph of Henry (3) and Arthur (1½).
Mrs D. Fowler

Family group at Evesham *c.* 1890. *Back row:* Jeannie, Arthur, Henry, Bessie. *Middle*: Henry (father), Mary (mother). *Front*: Alex, Molly, Charles.
Mrs D. Fowler

The Christmas card drawn by Arthur in 1898 for Henry. It shows the Bell Tower at Evesham. *Mrs D. Fowler*

Arthur Fowler showed an artistic bent, being sent to Birmingham Art School and began a career as an artist. However, he did not get fully established into this when he was taken quite seriously ill, became an invalid and died young. One of his artistic efforts survives in the form of a Christmas card designed for Henry in 1898, and is illustrated in this book. Other members of the family were also supplied with cards by Arthur.

The first record of an engineering bent in the Fowler family is to be found in John Fowler (b.1826), son of John Fowler (1792-1861) of Elm Grove near Melksham. John senior, after a period of time as a coal merchant, then became a successful tea merchant with a secondary hobby of farming. The story has been handed down concerning John junior trying out the first mowing machine that his father had acquired in a field known as Little Sands. The horses hitched to this machine were restive and clearly a bit disturbed by this mechanical contrivance. John senior said to his son: 'Ah, John, thee'll never get it to go'. 'Well, then, Father, I'll make it go', replied John junior, who a few years later was to acquire fame for his invention of the steam plough. He was to go on to found his own engineering company and acquire a knighthood for his exploits in this business.

With his father being a respected and long established local businessman, Henry was initially educated at the Grammar School, where his academic skills were noticed and encouraged by the teachers. His abilities on the mathematical and such sciences as were available were considerable and he was, at the age of 15, sent to the more specialised environment of the Mason Science College, Birmingham, to encourage these skills and the undoubted scientific interests that he had. The College was eventually to become part of the University of Birmingham such was its prowess in the scientific arts. Whilst at the College Henry's interest in one of the subjects studied, metallurgy, was aroused by the excellent treatment given by the lecturer, T. Turner - later Professor Turner at the University. Metallurgy was to remain a prime interest throughout his life and career.

In 1887, after two years at the College, at the end of which he received an Engineering Diploma, his engineering abilities demanded some 'hands-on' practical experience to put into practice the theoretical studies assimilated. In those days the best way to achieve this was by an apprenticeship with one of the major railway companies, which at that time were acknowledged to be at the forefront of mechanical engineering technology. They largely staffed their engineering departments with youngsters trained within their own workshops and at colleges and institutions funded by themselves.

The Lancashire & Yorkshire Railway was in the process of bringing its new Horwich works into operation, to replace the former facilities at Miles Platting which could not expand any further due to housing developments around the site. The main erection shop had opened in 1886, and in February 1887 the offices were ready for occupation. The Railway Mechanics Institute, which would provide the necessary theoretical classes to accompany the practical work in the workshops and offices, was in process of completion on the Chorley New Road, beside which the works were sited. Thus, with all the latest in equipment plus a nearby technical institute, all seemed set fair for those to be trained on the L&YR for an engineering career. John Aspinall, the current Chief Mechanical Engineer, was noted for his exceptional interest in apprentices and pupils should they show potential in their early days. He encouraged their prowess by personally taking them under his wing to nurture their skills with wise advice based on his own experiences.

So, under Aspinall, Henry Fowler began an apprenticeship which fitted him out for an auspicious future. His education continued at the Railway Mechanics Institute where his undoubted abilities were rewarded in 1891 when he obtained a Whitworth Exhibition, the first student at that establishment to do so.

A strapping young man of substantial physique, his time in the works made him familiar with the anatomy of the steam locomotive as he buckled down to assisting in the manufacture and assembly tasks required of him. His strong, thick, fingers made sure of a firm grip on the heavy components assigned to his care on the production line. He was a popular figure in the works, willing to converse with anyone, having the knack of putting them at their ease as soon as conversation began. He also was noted for his total abstinence from alcohol, and was to remain a committed tee-totaller for the whole of his life.

By now, Aspinall had recognised the potential of young Henry and taken him under his wing as a pupil. Other pupils with Aspinall at this time were George Hughes, Henry Hoy and Richard Maunsell, all of whom, like Fowler, were to rise to the top in the future. Here we have evidence that Henry's engineering skills had been noted by those in influential places.

As the final year of his apprenticeship began, Henry's metallurgical interests were noted by Aspinall, who ordered that he be placed in the Test Room, at that time in the charge of George Hughes who had finished his pupilage the previous year. This placing suited Henry's leaning towards these interests coupled with being a good training ground for his research aptitude. The time with Hughes was to result in a friendship which was to be of considerable use in later years when Hughes became, for a short time, CME of the LMS with Fowler as a deputy.

Concurrently with his appointment in the Test Room, Henry was appointed as a lecturer to some of their engineering classes by the Institute Committee. This was, in the main, evening work, so life was beginning to be busy. The employment of L&YR staff in the Institute followed the practice that many of the

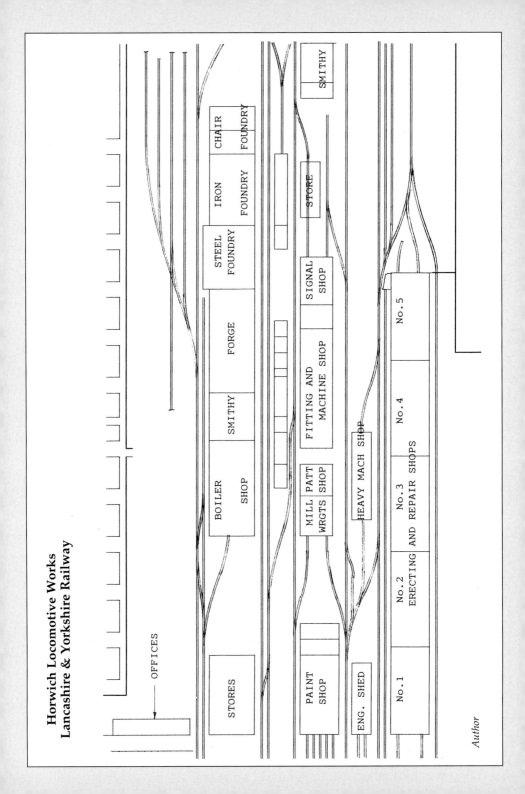

Horwich Locomotive Works
Lancashire & Yorkshire Railway

Author

railways employed in the Colleges or Institutes used, and often built, by them for the further education of the large number of apprentices they recruited.

In 1894, Hughes moved from the Test Room to other design matters and young Henry was appointed as chief inspector of materials in his place. The ladder was being climbed. His experience in the Test Room gave him a good early insight into the effects of the quality of materials on the failure of locomotives in service. His metallurgical interests were stimulated and sustained by this work and it was one aspect of locomotive work that was to remain of interest to him throughout his career.

At that time, with electric lighting a rarity, the railways employed gas lighting extensively for stations, shunting yards and goods facilities, engine sheds, repair shops, works and of course, passenger coaches. The lighting of the last-mentioned by gas was becoming widespread, this medium having displaced the earlier oil lighting. Several different systems were in use, in the main pressurised ones with the gas carried in strengthened tanks mounted on the underframes. It was simple to install and cheap to operate and was to remain a standard feature for many years until some spectacular accidents caused a gradual switch to electricity.

Henry Fowler showed an interest in the employment of gas as a lighting medium which was increased when, in addition to his Test Room responsibility, he was appointed to the position of Gas Manager. He also was, in his spare time, building up a friendship with Emma Needham Smith, a young lady from Horwich, who lived just along Victoria Road from Henry. Henry and Emma had come to meet in 1892 socially for the first time at Emma's 21st birthday celebrations, an event which Henry always remembered, as he wrote in later years . . .' How well I remember getting ready for your birthday. How I wondered what I could give you and how much I dare say. What a good time we had'. Emma's father, Philip Smith, was a chief clerk, which in those days was a not insubstantial post. Emma Smith was not ashamed of her early beginnings in a local mill, where she had worked from an early age, starting at six in the morning. She was a typical Lancashire lass, not afraid of hard work or straight talking and had a natural way of dealing with all walks of life, which, in later years, endeared her to the local communities in which she lived.

The friendship between Emma and Henry (Emmie and Harry to each other) was cemented at the 21st event and their meetings turned into a full-blown courtship. Henry finally plucked up the courage to pose the inevitable question and they were married on 26th June, 1895 at Trinity Church, Horwich and settled into home life in that town, now growing in size as the L&YR works provided a major source of employment for that area.

With a career beginning to formulate itself and the increased responsibilities accorded him, Henry was, on 15th April, 1896, elected to Associate Membership of the Institution of Mechanical Engineers. His proposer was, of course, John Aspinall and he was seconded by R.J. Smith with support from Henry Hoy, H.R. Thornton and Charles Allott. In the years to come he was to be much involved with this Institution as he was to be with the Institution of Civil Engineers, having joined the latter as a student member in 1896, amongst the many other bodies in the range of his many and varied interests. One of these interests was cycling. Henry probably had been encouraged by John Aspinall to encompass this as a means of obtaining exercise. Aspinall was himself a keen cyclist and, in the late 1890s took his daughter Edith on a cycling holiday in

Ireland, calling in on his 'old boy' Richard Maunsell, then Works Manager at the Inchicore works of the GS&WR.

By 1897 a few motor cars had appeared on the roads in Lancashire, as the law specifying a 4 mph speed limit, more commonly known as 'The Man With a Red Flag' Act, had been repealed the previous year and the few motorists around were able to exercise their steeds more freely. Henry was immediately attracted to this revolutionary mode of transport, particularly in connection with the problems associated with lighting the normally poorly lit roads when travelling at night. Acetylene gas was, in the early days of motoring, one medium to achieve satisfactory illumination. As this was also used by some of the railways its use on road vehicles drew Henry into a lifelong association with road transport. Always one for noting down his thoughts, he studied this form of lighting which culminated in a paper on 'Acetylene Gas Lighting' given at the Institution of Civil Engineers in 1897. This was the first of many papers to be read by him at the I.Civil.E. and I.Mech.E.

The interest in motor transport resulted in his being involved in the 1897 Crystal Palace Trials of motor vehicles. News of this obviously got back to Aspinall who, at that time, was becoming aware of the growth of short range mechanically-propelled vehicles and their potential impact on local goods services until then, provided by the railways.

In Liverpool some trials were to be made on heavy road cars (lorries) by the Liverpool Self-Propelled Traffic Association, instigated by Professor H.S. Hele-Shaw, who was at this time promoting a case for door-to-door transport using road vehicles. Aspinall arranged that Henry represented the L&YR at these trials, in order that a full account of the potential of road transport was reported to him at the earliest opportunity. He clearly saw the forthcoming competition of road transport and railways over short distances around towns. Both steam and internal combustion vehicles were involved in these trials.

Aspinall studied Fowler's reports carefully and could clearly see that any good motor vehicle would win on the terms of cost and immediacy in competition with a short rail journey which had the added complication of collection/delivery transfers at either end. He accordingly proposed that the L&YR buy a Thorneycroft steam powered motor-wagon for some trials, which was approved in 1900.

The interest aroused in Fowler by this exercise into the potential of road transport, plus some comments of Aspinall concerning the inevitability of the motor car, caused him to get himself involved in the ownership of early vehicles. He, like other railway officials, could begin to see what lay ahead, the motor-car invasion and its corresponding effects upon railway passenger traffic. Other means of public transport around towns, such as the electric tram, were also beginning to make their presence felt.

Notwithstanding his already full timetable, Henry joined the Institution of Automobile Engineers at the earliest opportunity. Life at home was also becoming more crowded, with the arrival of Emma and Henry's first son, also Henry, in 1897.

It was in 1898 that a new pupil of Aspinall appeared from Crewe to round off his experience before setting out on the management path. This was Nigel Gresley who, after a spell in the drawing office, was put in charge of the Materials Test Room, as Fowler was now so busy with his Gas Engineer's and Research posts. The research side of things was tied up with Aspinall's plan to carry out a series of comprehensive experiments on train resistance. The gas matters being well under control, Aspinall suggested that Henry let them look after their own ends and apply his expertise and clear research abilities to arranging the test programme. As assistant he was given the help of a Mr A.C. Rogerson.

The first task falling to Henry was the design and construction of a dynamometer car capable of measuring the pull loads and speeds of the trains involved, as well as that important feature affecting train speed, that of wind direction and velocity. The car was duly built and the test gear installed for calibration before the trials began in earnest in May 1899. Aspinall's recognition of the importance of wind speed and direction on train resistance showed his keen engineering perception, never before had any meaningful attempt been made to account for this factor. Aerodynamics was in its infancy and any attempt to assess the effects of airflow around moving bodies was most certainly pioneering, and must have appealed to Henry Fowler's active mind. The special train commenced running to gather data between Southport and Wigan between June 1899 and January 1900. Five trains were made up ranging from 5 to 29 bogie coaches, being hauled by one of Aspinall's 2-4-2 radial tanks. The results were written up by Henry and his assistant and presented to Aspinall, who subsequently used them in the presentation of a paper which was given on 26th November, 1901 at the Institution of Civil Engineers. This paper won for Aspinall the 1902 Watt medal and was the first one to cover comprehensively the variation due to wind resistance caused by the wind direction relative to that of the train itself. The discussion that ensued from this paper took up most of the following evening and added some 22 figures to the 42 contained in the paper itself. By the time that Fowler's tests had been presented in this paper, he had moved elsewhere. His contribution to the contents, however, was duly noted.

In early 1900, Samuel Johnson, the Locomotive Superintendent of the Midland Railway mentioned to John Aspinall that he was looking for new technical staff and required someone to look after research and take responsibility for the gas department, the latter under the control of J. Reid, who was about to retire. Aspinall cast his mind to his staff at Horwich and mentioned that Henry Fowler might be interested in such an opportunity. Advancement on the L&YR for such as Fowler was likely to be slow with people such as Hoy, Hughes, and Gresley around, the former two to shortly be CME and Works Manager respectively and Gresley to become Assistant Manager of the carriage and wagon works at Newton Heath. So it seemed likely that a move elsewhere might be of benefit to the other 'old boy' as Aspinall often referred to his bright ex-pupils. As Johnson was approaching retirement, the prospect of advancement at Derby was much greater. Aspinall himself was only 49 and had just been promoted to General Manager of the L&YR and many of the key people were still a long way from retirement, so further advancement at Horwich seemed remote.

Although comfortably established at Horwich, the possibility of quicker advancement offered Fowler a good chance for his future and he applied to the MR for the opening as Manager in the gas department. He got the job, and responsibility for overseeing the Testing area as well, not surprisingly, with Johnson primed by Aspinall regarding his keenness and abilities in those fields.

And so, in 1900 Henry, Emma and the family moved to Derby, setting up home at No 122, Rose Hill Street. Derby and its immediate locality was to be their home for the rest of their lives. It was a short walk to the Midland Railway works which stood between the railway station and the canal, where Henry commenced his new employment in the design and works offices situated in the building, with its distinctive turret clock tower atop the three floors, adjacent to the original roundhouse built for the North Midland Railway in 1842. This building still exists today, as does the roundhouse, and the tower is visible across the rooftops of Derby. The clock itself is apparantly the last one made by the local firm of Whitehurst of Derby. This fact was noted by a former apprentice to Whitehurst, one John Smith, founder of the Midland Clock Works which eventually became the birthplace of the trade name Smith Sectric.

No. 122, Rose Hill Street, Derby.   *Author*

Chapter Two

The Rise to CME 1900-1910

Henry Fowler commenced his new responsibilities at Derby on 16th June. The MR works were busy turning out the final 10 of Johnson's elegant 4-2-2s, or 'Spinners' as they were better known. Train weights were still low enough for the employment of single driving wheels, particularly if steam sanding gear was fitted, although as the new century progressed they were to grow such that 'singles' could no longer cope.

Henry settled into his Gas Engineer and Chief of the Testing Department position, at a salary of £350, and obviously made his presence felt, for his abilities were most certainly noticed by Johnson and Deeley, the latter shortly to become Works Manager. An initial foray into the local community was some lecturing at the Derby Technical College, as soon as it was found that his earlier experience at the Horwich Institute was relevant.

He would, once established in the Rose Hill Street house, have entered the works over the recently opened footbridge from Hulland Street, which had been requested as far back as 1883 but not approved until 1896 by the General Purposes Committee of the MR.

Meantime, the works were engaged in building large numbers of Johnson's new large 4-4-0s of the '700' class. These locomotives were intended for use on the Settle-Carlisle line and were sufficiently powerful to handle the trains of that day unassisted, thus reducing double-heading. This class also employed the Belpaire boiler for the first time on the Midland, Johnson resolutely refusing to employ this feature for some time (since 1875 in fact!) as; 'I like to be sure and on the safe side'. Extreme caution was his watchword where new developments were concerned. The first 35 of the 50 turned out in 1900-04 had a large bogie tender with a water capacity of 4,500 gallons which, when fully laden, actually weighed more than the engine itself.

In parallel with this 4-4-0 expansion, the first of the compounds, for which the Midland was to become famous, entered service in November 1901. Four more were outshopped in 1902. This design, and variants of it, was destined to be in production for 30 years.

Johnson's final design to reach production was a new form of his standard 0-6-0 goods locomotive, with 20 appearing in 1903. The Locomotive Drawing Office (LDO) was also busy finalising the drawings for two more widely differing types, firstly an outside cylindered 0-8-0 goods engine and secondly a 4-4-4T passenger tank. A complete set of drawings for both were prepared, but neither type appeared, the 0-8-0 being replaced by plans for more smaller engines and the 4-4-4T, for which an order for 10 was placed, was cancelled. Johnson was close to retirement and these final upsets did not worry him unduly.

And so, at the end of 1903, Johnson retired, his place being taken by Deeley from his position as Works Manager. The new Works Manager was Cecil Paget, the son of the MR Chairman, Sir Ernest Paget, Bart. The stage was now set for a clash at the top, which was to result in Henry Fowler being well placed to move dramatically up to the top position.

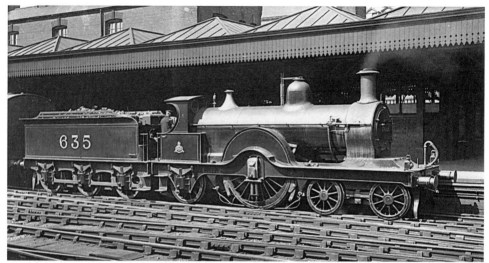

Johnson '1P' class 4-2-2 'Spinner' No. 635 is seen at Nottingham Midland *c.* 1926, still sporting its Midland Railway livery.   *Rail Archive Stephenson*

The year before Fowler arrived at Derby, the Works were busy assembling a batch of American supplied 2-6-0s ordered as a stop-gap to fill a desperate need for more locomotives which could not be supplied in time from Derby or outside contractors in Britain. This photograph also shows the main office block where Fowler would have had his offices over the years. The footbridge seen passed over the Midland Railway main lines to Derby station.

Derby Industrial Museum

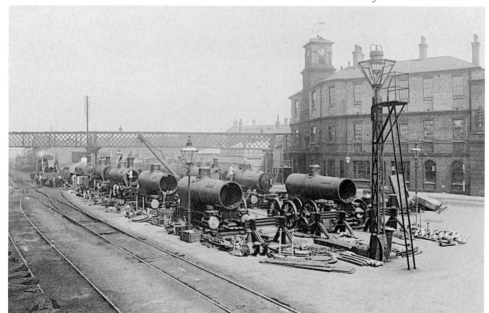

MR '3P' 4-4-0 No. 758 is seen leaving Elstree tunnel with the 1.00 pm St Pancras to Sheffield express in 1925.   *Rail Archive Stephenson*

One of the many departments on Fowler's tours of inspection as Works Manager would have been the old No. 1 roundhouse. It is depicted here in 1905. The building still stands and is the oldest roundhouse in the world.   *Derby Industrial Museum*

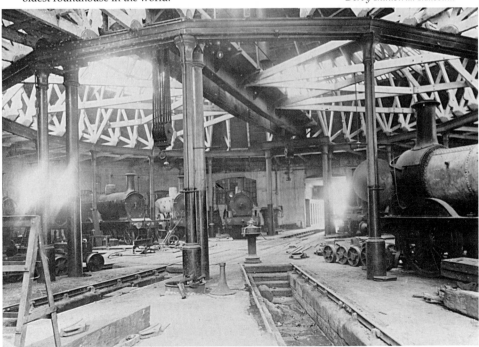

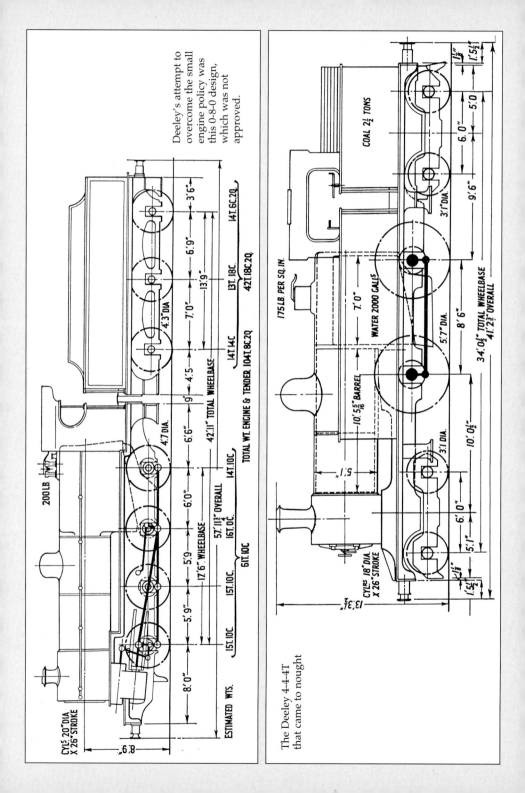

Deeley's attempt to overcome the small engine policy was this 0-8-0 design, which was not approved.

The Deeley 4-4-4T that came to nought

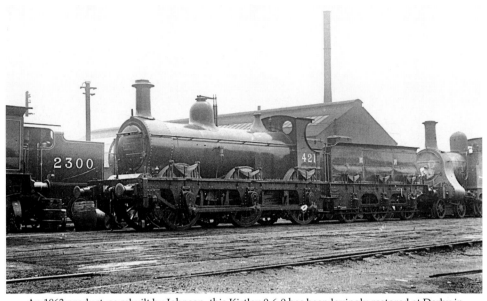

An 1863 product, as rebuilt by Johnson, this Kirtley 0-6-0 has been lovingly restored at Derby in 1929, only to be cut up by Stanier in 1932. Behind this can be seen an old North London Railway 4-4-0T, which underwent the same fate.   *R.S. Carpenter Collection*

Johnson '3F' class 0-6-0s as rebuilt by Deeley in the early 1900s were long-lived. Here No. 3183 passes Market Harborough with an up freight in the 1940s.   *A.V.W. Mace Collection*

Johnson 3-cylinder compound No. 2635 in original condition at Kentish Town.   *Lens of Sutton*

Compound No. 1025, of the 1906 batch built under Deeley on a leisurely task in 1930.
Maunsell Locomotive Society Collection

Paget was to become famous for his attempt to develop a radical new rotary valve concept for the steam locomotive, and had enjoyed a meteoric rise to the Works Manager position at the age of 30. He had been educated at Harrow, started an apprenticeship at Derby Works, then left to go to Cambridge from where he returned to Derby and his rapid rise. He was a mechanical experimenter of considerable skill and his scheme for the new valve was based on that of achieving steam distribution by a rotary sleeve valve instead of the normal reciprocating type. He put his idea to Deeley, who would not consider it, being steeped in the Johnson cautious approach to new ideas. Therefore he decided to go ahead on his own at his own expense, outside the MR design organisation. He accordingly set up a small design office in Derby in 1904, engaging James Clayton and Herbert Chambers in a private capacity as designers/draughtsmen. Deeley looked upon this with considerable suspicion, for he saw that Paget was well placed to make a bid for his job should he retire from the scene - after all, Paget's father *was* the Chairman and the rule, up to now, had been for the Works Manager to step into the Locomotive Superintendent's shoes!

The year 1903 had been one of tragedy for the Fowlers. Harry, now aged six, was joined by Geoffrey Phillip, born on 16th March of that year. However, his new little brother died on 20th October, at the age of just seven months. Henry and Emma were heartbroken by their loss, but the strong Christian faith which was such an important part of their lives carried them through the sad days. Little Geoffrey was buried at the Nottingham Road cemetery in Derby in the plot purchased by Henry and which, eventually, was to be his and Emma's final resting place.

Whilst this was all taking place, Henry Fowler was busy involving himself in the Christian meetings which took place around the Works. To this end he began to hold a short religious service for those interested, in the No. 3 mess room,during the breakfast break at the start of the day. This mess room had, for some time, been fitted out with a pulpit and organ for such a purpose. Photographs of the room also show large pictures depicting biblical scenes adorning the walls. His strong Christian beliefs, encouraged by his strict upbringing, were evident in this involvement, which undoubtedly brought a measure of respect from many quarters.

In October 1904, the Fowler family expanded with the safe arrival of a daughter, Dorothea, to join young Henry, now seven years old. It was around this time that the Fowlers moved from their first home in Rose Hill Street to Chellaston, on the southern outskirts of the city. It was a grander house, 'The Hollies', needed to accommodate the growing family, but was some three miles from the railway works. However, a short walk down Station Road brought Henry to the station on the branch line which connected with the main line into Derby.

Meantime, Paget continued his private design exercise, being appointed to the position of Assistant Locomotive Superintendent on 1st November, 1905. This was in addition to his current Works Manager's position. Deeley viewed this with some alarm, as here was the Chairman's son and experimenter in a position to succeed him, should he go. Politically, this was not a desirable outcome and it appears that some of the Board had similar feelings and obviously mentioned their thoughts to Sir Ernest Paget. The result was that, although the Paget locomotive would continue to be built as time and space was available in the busy works, there were other more pressing matters needing the attention of someone with an astute mind of the calibre of Cecil Paget.

A painting of 'The Hollies' at Chellaston.   *British Legion, Chellaston Branch*

In May 1907, Henry Fowler was appointed Works Manager in place of Paget, who was given the newly created position of General Superintendent. This was a wide-ranging job, giving him a general command over all the departments at Derby. He busied himself in many areas, firstly, to encourage a larger number of apprentices with good educational backgrounds he instigated a premium apprentice scheme. Henry Fowler thoroughly approved of this, it meant that he would have a better calibre of trainees from which to choose his staff. He always was to take an keen interest in the training of the future engineers for the MR and, later, the LMS.

Paget also made it his job to tour Derby works and institute a major reorganisation of the stores system employed for the issue and recording of tools and equipment. On the office side he had the piles of paper that tended to accumulate in odd corners cleared up, followed by a complete redecoration of the offices. This latter eliminated the rather forbidding decor for a brighter, cleaner, image which was much appreciated by the staff.

Finally, he was packed off to the USA to find out about systems for centralised train control in use over there, and decide whether they could be used to advantage by the MR. Problems with the extensive coal traffic on the railway were such that some better means of control were badly needed. The lengthy and slow trains comprising this traffic had frequently to be parked in loops alongside the main line for considerable periods so that passenger traffic of short frequent trains could keep to time. It was not unknown for these coal trains to be stabled thus for many hours, sometimes long enough for a crew to book on and off without turning a wheel! Hardly a recipe for efficient operation.

Paget's visit to the USA was specifically to see their train control system in operation and upon his return his father backed up his plans to adopt what he had seen in operation onto the MR. His research before instigating the new system was painstaking - spending long periods of time in an inspection coach parked at specific traffic bottle-necks to gather the data needed for analysis and implementation. The old MR Boardroom suite of 1872, next to the shareholders' room at Derby Station was converted into the main train control room in 1907-08, and from the Victorian splendour of this old room Paget inaugurated his American-inspired system. He was, by this, effectively removed from the lineage leading to the Locomotive Superintendentcy.

However, Henry had only a short time to settle into his Works Manager's shoes, as he was dispatched off to North America on a fact-finding tour. This was, at this time, a very fashionable thing to do, with many other major railways sending key personnel over to see what could be gleaned from the railways on that continent. Whilst he was away, James Anderson, the chief locomotive draughtsman, was ordered to cover for him. Anderson will be cropping up later in our story, a great proponent of the Midland small engine policy, he had a profound influence on how matters progressed throughout Fowler's time at the top.

Around this time, on his journeys to and from the works, Henry would have noticed the beginnings of a new factory growing on the northern edge of Sinfin Moor, just east of his route. This was to become the large Rolls-Royce plant which in later years produced, not only the famous cars, but thousands of aero engines for both World Wars, and indeed today is still a major producer of the units that power many types of jet transports the World over.

The additional locomotives to come in Deeley's time were, in the main, for passenger work. The existing fleet of goods types (nearly all 0-6-0s) of previous designers were being rebuilt and upgraded to satisfy traffic needs in that area. The most famous design to come from Deeley was his compound, being a derivative of Johnson's original design, the first batch being turned out in 1905. Deeley altered the design in respect of the steam distribution by arranging that when the regulator was partially opened the engine worked simple, further opening then closed an auxiliary valve which switched the engine to compound working. Upon entering service these compounds immediately proved a success and further batches were authorised, 20 in 1906 and 10 in 1908.

A conventional 4-4-0, the '990' class, was also built by Deeley, as a comparison with the compound, but any meaningful results were rather negated by the employment of Deeley's own valve gear on this class.

So far as experimental work was concerned, all Deeley is recorded as having instigated was one conversion of a 4-4-0, No. 232, to employ Marshall's valve gear, which resulted in no material change to performance or economy, and eventually the locomotive reverted to its original condition.

The last design to come from Deeley which was to enter service was his 0-6-4T for local passenger work. Never a very successful locomotive, due to instability at moderate to high speeds, 40 were built in 1907 and distributed over the MR system.

Henry established himself in his Works Manager rôle, and began planning for some changes in the shops, which he used to tour on a regular basis by bicycle, often wearing a straw hat. The story is told of his cycle wheel becoming trapped in one of the many rails in the shop floors, resulting in a rather undignified dismounting, with the straw hat spinning off at an angle. Henry ruefully straightened himself up, collected his hat, remounted, and continued his tour at a more sedate pace, trying not to notice the obvious merriment of the workers who had witnessed the event.

His tours of the works were noted for his continual look-out for bad behaviour or shoddy work practices. If noticed by his searching gaze, the culprits were ordered to clock off and return as normal the next day. The loss of

Deeley 0-6-4T No. 2006 going strong with a local passenger near Derby *c.* 1923. Note the preponderance of six-wheeled stock still in service.   *John Scott-Morgan Collection*

In later years some of the Deeley 0-6-4Ts were rebuilt with Belpaire boilers by Fowler in 1925. Here No. 2022 is caught at Manchester Central on a local passenger not long before it was withdrawn in 1935.   *John Scott-Morgan Collection*

up to a day's pay was, in those days, a strong deterrent to further misbehaviour. Those subjected to this form of discipline were, Henry reckoned, less likely to bear a grudge for long. In those days of strict industrial rules, this somewhat lenient approach certainly appeared to be effective. As a Works Manager his energetic tours and meticulous inspections of conditions on the shop floor were a notable feature of his management style.

For some time now Henry had been playing hockey for Derbyshire and the Midland Counties, his sporting prowess making him a useful member of the teams. As his age was now getting to the limit for team membership, he kept his involvement in hockey current by taking up umpiring, subsequently being elected to the England Selection Board for that sport. His cricketing continued unabated, and was to do so for most of the rest of his life.

As all the aforementioned had been taking place, the Paget locomotive had been completed, the final costs being borne by the MR, as Paget had by now run out of his funds. At some time in 1908, some trials took place between Derby and Leicester. Little evidence of the results survives, save that it is reported that a speed in excess of 80 mph was achieved with a 300 ton train. However, the sleeve valves, as with Bulleid's 'Leader' of the late 1940s, were to prove troublesome, the problem being differential expansion causing seizure and failure. By now Cecil Paget was fully engaged on implementing the findings of his North American trip and the resulting train control exercise, and the experimental locomotive was brought back to Derby Works and stored in a corner, under tarpaulins, to await its fate.

However, moves were afoot to restructure the top management responsibilities on the MR. Deeley was called into a Directors' meeting in 1909 and informed that the position of Locomotive Superintendent was to be split between that of Chief Mechanical Engineer, who would cover research, design and production, and that of Chief Motive Power Superintendent to cover supply, maintenance and operating matters.

Deeley was, to put it mildly, more than a bit upset at this and suggested that it would be better if two new men were appointed and tendered his resignation. After he and the Directors had come to an amicable agreement, including a generous life pension, he left the MR on 13th August, 1909. He had, just prior to this, instructed the LDO to prepare drawings of a 4-6-0 version of the compound, but this was quickly squashed, on his resignation, by Anderson, who still appeared determined to pursue the small engine policy.

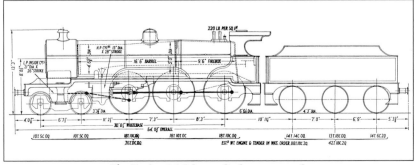

The Deeley 4-6-0 four-cylinder compound.

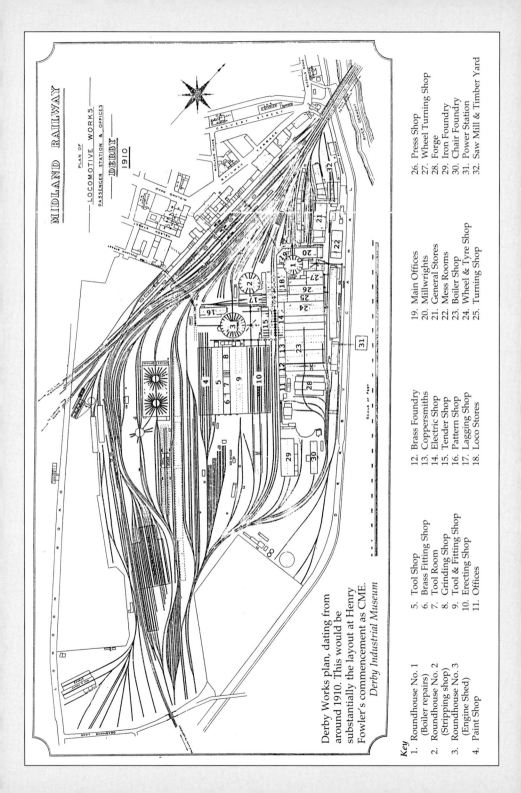

MIDLAND RAILWAY

PLAN OF
— LOCOMOTIVE WORKS —
PASSENGER STATION & OFFICES
— DERBY —
1910

Derby Works plan, dating from around 1910. This would be substantially the layout at Henry Fowler's commencement as CME.

Derby Industrial Museum

Key

1. Roundhouse No. 1
   (Boiler repairs)
2. Roundhouse No. 2
   (Stripping shop)
3. Roundhouse No. 3
   (Engine Shed)
4. Paint Shop
5. Tool Shop
6. Brass Fitting Shop
7. Tool Room
8. Grinding Shop
9. Tool & Fitting Shop
10. Erecting Shop
11. Offices
12. Brass Foundry
13. Coppersmiths
14. Electric Shop
15. Tender Shop
16. Pattern Shop
17. Lagging Shop
18. Loco Stores
19. Main Offices
20. Millwrights
21. General Stores
22. Mess Rooms
23. Boiler Shop
24. Wheel & Tyre Shop
25. Turning Shop
26. Press Shop
27. Wheel Turning Shop
28. Forge
29. Iron Foundry
30. Chair Foundry
31. Power Station
32. Saw Mill & Timber Yard

The problem now for the Board was who should be appointed as CME. Some weeks of deliberation ensued and eventually, due to his competent handling of his responsibilities as Works Manager, Henry Fowler was appointed to the position. That of the vacant Works Manager was given to James Anderson, who for the following three years also retained his chief locomotive draughtsman's responsibilities. This gave him a good foundation to build on in his desire to continue the MR small engine policy, which was to cause much disruption later, in the early days of the LMS.

So, on 1st January, 1910, Henry Fowler reached the pinnacle of his profession. He was 39 years of age, industrious, yet easy-going enough for the Board to realise that no major policy upsets would emanate from his office. He had under his control, some 20 acres of workshops and offices, and was responsible for the servicing of 2,970 locomotives, amassing 48 million miles and burning 1 million tons of coal per year, of which some 1,300 passed through the shops each year in addition to new production. To achieve this there was a workforce of 4,264 men plus 383 foremen, clerks and draughtsmen. The iron foundry had a weekly capacity of some 420 tons, and the machine shops employed 570 machines of all kinds, from the simple pillar drill to the large wheel and tyre profiling lathes. The erecting shops could hold 72 locomotives at any one time. The overseeing of all this was a formidable task.

Just prior the the appointment, Henry had been planning for a radical change in the works, this being the switch to electricity as a power and lighting source. He quickly got things under way, for by May 1910 Order No. 3716 was issued for the construction of a new power station on the far side of the Derby Canal to the works. A Mr Dalziel, given the post of Electrical Assistant, drew up the specification for the 3,000kW capacity turbine-driven generators.

Before the new power station was in operation, the current needed for operation of the newly installed and modified machines and equipment was obtained from the Nottingham Electric Power Company. Henry had two new 50 ton capacity electric cranes installed in the Erecting Shop to replace the old and slow shaft driven units. The works was much improved, and production rates boosted by this modernisation.

His elevation to CME produced an invitation to join the Association of Railway Locomotive Engineers (ARLE), a select body made up of all those in similar positions, which met two or three times a year to discuss topics of mutual interest. He was welcomed at the 1910 summer meeting by Wilson Worsdell of the North Eastern Railway. Deeley, although a member of this group, had rarely attended the meetings. Henry Fowler was to become greatly involved in ARLE matters in future years.

On the research side, some experiments with alternative valve gears were authorised by Fowler in 1910-11, 4-4-0s Nos. 382 and 387 being fitted with Isaacson's and a MR modified Stephenson's gear respectively for comparison with the unmodified No. 379. No worthwhile benefit for the experimental gear was forthcoming in terms of coal or water consumption and the series of tests terminated with the locomotives being returned to standard configuration.

By September, a scheme for an inside cylinder 2-6-0 had appeared on the board in the LDO, but little interest, coupled to Anderson's dislike of even this moderate sized locomotive, could be generated and it died.

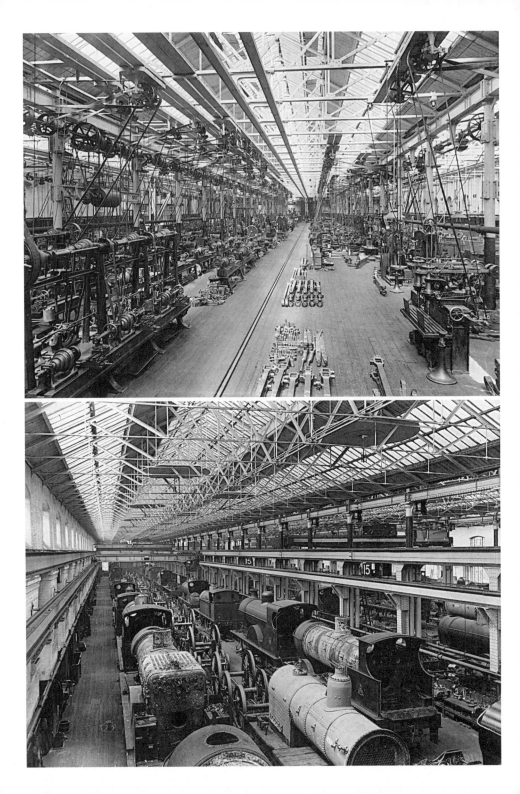

Above: All that remains of the original railway works of 1839, the old office block sits in front of the first roundhouse, which is now preserved to remind one of the railway heritage at Derby.
Author

Top left: The machine shop in 1910.   *National Railway Museum*

Bottom left: Just after Fowler took office as CME, the erecting shop at Derby Works is found full of locomotives under repair or construction.   *National Railway Museum*

Below: Midland Railway Institute, Derby, still in immaculate condition in 1999.   *Author*

The 1911 summer meeting of the ARLE, held at the Central Hotel, Glasgow, was attended by Fowler, who to aid the discussion proposed on the differentiation of costs of heavy and light repairs to locomotives, submitted the current Midland practice for consideration. Broadly, the MR locomotive costs were apportioned as follows:

1. New engines
2. Reboilered engines
3. Heavy shop repairs classified as: boiler removal from the frames, new crank axle fitted, four or more new tyres fitted
4. Light shop repairs classified as: new cylinders, new straight axles, patching frames, more than half the tubes replaced, turning wheels and metalling boxes. Two or more of these would be classed as a heavy repair.
5. Shed repairs

With the majority of the goods fleet of 0-6-0s now somewhat dated (none were superheated at that time) and needing replacement, Fowler had the LDO scheming an improved version of the standard saturated design currently in service. The resulting locomotive was to be the '4F', a design to be in production for some 30 years, until 772 had been built, such was its usefulness and versatility. Two prototypes were built in 1911 for extensive trials. They employed superheating from the outset, one example, No. 3835, having the Schmidt type and No. 3836 the Swindon double-pass type. Fowler wished to compare the two types of superheater before settling which one to standardise on. The boiler was the 'G7S' type, developed for the Deeley rebuilds of the class '2' 4-4-0s. Initially, they had steam reversers.

Some trials on the two '4Fs' were carried out in 1912, to compare their performance with the standard unsuperheated 0-6-0 it was to supersede. They were put to work, over a five week period, on the Toton-Brent coal trains, 600 tons up and 50 to 100 empties down. The Schmidt superheater version, No. 3835, came out best, showing a 20 per cent saving in coal and 25 per cent saving in water when compared to the saturated engines.

The '4F' became, probably, the most successful of Fowler's designs, and was to be found all over the MR (and subsequently, the LMS) on a wide range of duties, having a wide route availability. However, train weights were still increasing, and so the '4F' was frequently found being piloted by an older 0-6-0 on many of the coal trains and, in later years as it became more prolific, by another '4F'. Although powerful for its size, the 4F could not eliminate that common Midland trait, the double-header.

Henry's old colleague, Richard Maunsell, now Locomotive Superintendent of the Great Southern & Western Railway of Ireland (GS&WR), had been invited to become a member of the ARLE in late 1911, being proposed by fellow Irishman, Bowman Malcolm of the Northern Counties Committee (NCC) (part of the Midland's Railway's empire) and seconded by Fowler. The old friendship between Fowler and Maunsell was to be strengthened at the following meetings, a friendship which was to have a significant effect on Derby locomotive policy in the early days of the LMS.

Chapter Three

Consolidation at Derby and War

In the early years of Fowler's appointment as CME his earlier responsibilities as Gas Manager were long forgotten, until two spectacular accidents occurred on the MR which must have raised old memories in his mind.

The employment of gas lighting on carriages was still in widespread use, having long superseded the earlier oil lighting, which was described by one contemporary report as that which 'merely made the darkness visible'. Whilst electric lighting was available, and indeed had been applied in a limited extent by many railway companies, the London, Brighton & South Coat Railway as far back as 1885, the attraction of gas was its cheapness, effective lighting and general low maintenance costs. The specialised art of providing adequate light at an economic cost outweighed the potential for disaster in the minds of many railway Boards.

Henry Fowler, in his Gas Engineer days had been in constant search of even more efficient gas systems to install in the trains. The type of system prevalent during his time on the MR in that capacity was the Pintsch oil gas lighting, the fuel for which was contained in pressurised tanks at some 65 psi mounted on the underframes.

The lethal combination of a pressurised container being punctured in an accident combined with coals from locomotive ashpans or sparks from tortured metal on ballast was ignored in the interests of economy. Indeed there had been accidents in the past which had not resulted in fires due to the foresight of those involved in rescue operations, notably the Poulton derailment of 1891 when Richard Maunsell, who was present and witnessed the incident, ordered the gas tanks to be punctured and the gas released before any fires were lit to assist in the rescue and clearing up operation (this accident happened at 11 pm).

The MR, under Fowler, was firmly into gas lighting even though warning signs were evident. The first portent of major disaster had happened at Wellingborough in 1898 when the 7.15 pm dining car express from St Pancras was derailed by a porter's trolley which had rolled off the platform into its path. Of the 65 passengers on board five were killed and 60 injured. One of the carriages caught fire due to a gas leak from a damaged tank. Although this fire did not lead directly to any of the deaths or injuries, the warning was there of future tragedy.

It was 24th December, 1910 before catastrophy struck, at Hawes Junction, on the Settle and Carlisle line. The St Pancras to Glasgow sleeper express collided at speed with two light engines at 5.44 am. The signalman at Hawes Junction box had forgotten the light engines and, when pulling the signals to clear the express, they had taken off at moderate speed, having neglected to apply Rule 55, that of reminding the signalman of their presence.

Twelve people died in the crash with many seriously injured, mainly by the blaze that ensued from gas pouring from fractured tanks. The report of this accident wound up by reminding the Midland Railway of the dangers of gas

Right: 'The Homestead', the Fowler's first home in Spondon, which still stands today, in use as a high class hotel and restaurant.

Author

Below: Spondon Cricket Club First XI, 1914, Henry Fowler as Captain.

Spondon Historical Society

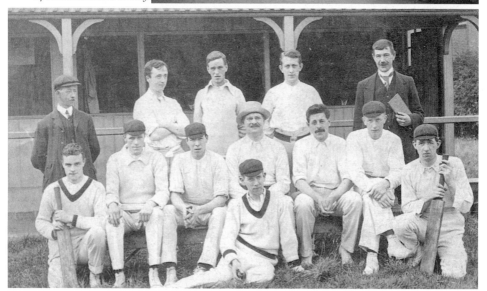

lighting. Fowler was now CME and, although the current Gas Engineer came under his remit so far as the technical side of things go, little appears to have been done to remedy the situation.

Nearly three years passed, and then a further accident on the Settle and Carlisle line at Ais Gill produced another gas-fuelled fire in which 14 passengers perished and 38 were injured. The speed at which the fires had gripped the stricken trains pointed to the need to finish with gas lighting and the switch to electricity then came, albeit incredibly slowly, for in 1927 a further accident at Lytham, a derailment caused by a locomotive tyre breaking and fouling the track, resulted in a gas fire which was responsible for many of the 14 deaths.

As CME, Henry had the opportunity to augment his salary by means of pupilage fees. One of his first pupils was C.E. Fairburn who, having achieved three Firsts at Oxford, decided to further his engineering interests at the Derby works. Fairburn was to have four years with the MR before joining up to fight in 1914, having a distinguished war career, after which he joined the English Electric Company in 1919. He eventually rose to become Manager and Engineer of the Traction Department, and was to return to the railway scene in 1934 as Electrical Engineer of the LMS, subsequently becoming CME in 1944.

So far as family matters were concerned, the 22nd June, 1911 brought about the birth of Henry and Emma's third son, George Eric, to be known as Eric within the family, who was a welcome addition to the fold. George Eric was a robust youngster, who always was to have a special place in Henry's heart, as if he made up for the tragic loss of baby Geoffrey in 1903. Henry junior's reaction was not recorded, he was now a strapping 14-year-old who had just commenced his higher education at Oundle in May of that year, and was thinking about a possible career in the near future.

Commensurate with his elevation to the top position in the Locomotive Department, Henry cast around for a more suitable home, now that his salary was at a considerably increased amount. The village, as it was then, of Spondon lay two miles from the railway works, on the eastern outskirts of Derby and central to this was an imposing house, 'The Homestead'. This large Georgian house was built by a member of the Anthill family around 1720. It eventually passed by marriage to the Cade family, who lived there for over a hundred years until they vacated it in 1911, when it became available for rent. Henry and Emma viewed it and assessed the local area. Spondon had a thriving cricket club whose ground lay a couple of hundred yards from the house. This club had been founded in 1883 and originally played on the Spondon House School ground. It absorbed the Spondon West End cricket club in 1903 and moved to vacant ground between Mill Row and Windsor Lane, just up the hill from 'The Homestead'. This same year the club joined the Derby and District League. In 1908, before the Fowlers appeared on the scene, a new pavilion was opened by Sir Herbert Raphael, MP for South Derbyshire. The club flourishes to this day, with a much improved pavilion provided in 1969 and is one of the few village clubs in the country to own the ground on which it plays. Also, no Sunday cricket was played at Spondon, a fact which would have pleased Henry considerably, as that day was to be reserved for Church and the Bible Study class.

The Parish Church of St Werburgh's was a short walk down Sitwell Street, so involvement and attendance at that was easy, the MR works were a short drive along the Nottingham Road, across the River Derwent, through Derby centre to the Siddals Road entrance. Alternatively, Henry could cycle the half mile down to Spondon station and get the train direct into Derby station or, as he often did in good weather, cycle the whole way to the works.

Weighing all this up, Henry decided upon Spondon as the family's new home and they moved into 'The Homestead' and established themselves in what was then a village.

One of the first things Henry did, once settled, was to join the cricket club. When the other members realised his sporting abilities it was not long before he was playing for the first eleven, eventually to captain it for some years.

'The Homestead' was to be their home for the following seven years and see them well established as an influential family of considerable local esteem, more particularly after World War I. The house still stands, being one of only three Grade 1 listed buildings in the City of Derby and is currently in use as a high class country house hotel and restaurant.

In January 1912, the MR took over the London, Tilbury and Southend Railway (LT&SR), and Fowler, in August of that year, found himself in charge of the locomotive policy of that railway. A considerable amount of effort had to be put into shopping many of the LT&SR locomotives, which were in rather a run-down condition. Some urgent reboilering took place and Fowler ordered that plans be made to incorporate various standard fittings as the occasion permitted to 'Midlandise' these, largely 4-4-2T, types.

LT&SR 4-4-2T No. 2111 after treatment for fitment of Fowler standard parts, most notable being the chimney, on repairs carried out at Derby.   *John Scott-Morgan Collection*

1912 was a full year so far as Henry's society obligations were concerned, firstly he was elected to the Presidency of the Institution of Locomotive Engineers, followed by the Presidency of the University of Birmingham Engineering Society. The University had grown, in part, from the Mason Science College, which had given him his basic engineering studies prior to his apprenticeship at Horwich, and was rightly proud of its past pupil's rise to the top. He also increased his involvement in the affairs of the I.Mech.E. with membership of the Advisory Committees for Cutting Tools, Welding and Research.

The November 1912, meeting of the ARLE found Fowler being put onto a standing committee on screw thread standards for the engineering industries. The ARLE had been represented by Gresley, Pickersgill and Robinson, but the last mentioned was too busy to attend, and Fowler, with his metallurgical interests, was the logical replacement. He needed little encouragement to add this extra demand to his already full responsibilities.

In keeping with the still current trend to visit the United States, Henry Fowler made his second such trip in the summer of 1913. He sailed on the RMS *Mauretania* on Saturday 31st May, and the voyage was described in some detail in a letter to the members of his Bible Class. On the Sunday morning:

> When I woke up, or rather got up, this morning we were lying outside Queenstown (Cobh) harbour and a tug was coming out to us with passengers and hundreds of mail bags. For a long time there was a continuous stream of men fetching these onto the boat as fast as they could go. As soon as they had finished we were off along the South coast of Ireland - about 12 o'clock we went by the Fastnet rock which I suppose is about 6 or 8 miles from the shore . . .

After this he had attended the morning service, taken that Sunday by the Purser, followed by a turn on deck where he watched the coast slip by. After leaving the lee of Ireland it began to blow and rain. The following day the sea had got up and the ship was rolling and pitching quite badly, which made him sea-sick: 'I was ill enough to feel that the best place for me was my berth and nothing to eat the best food' he reported. By the next day things were quieting down and he was up late in the morning and had a good lunch. The ship was on a course south of west, as the shipping companies, mindful of the previous year's disaster with the *Titanic*, carefully avoided the more northerly waters with their fogs and icebergs. However, the storm of the previous day had caused a reduction of speed and the fog which they were now running into restricted their progress somewhat, as he reported on the Thursday: 'I had quite expected that I should have been in New York this afternoon but it will be well on tomorrow morning before we land . . .' Henry passed the time by playing shuffle-board and taking long walks round the decks. They had not seen any other vessels for some time, when 300 miles off New York, the White Star liner *Baltic* was spotted ahead on a similar course. They berthed in New York about half a day overdue and Henry gladly stepped ashore on dry land to commence his investigations and travels. The letter describing his journey was posted at the ocean terminal and would have come back on the *Mauretania's* return voyage.

It was in 1913 that a battery locomotive was built at Derby for shunting work at the MR coal depot at West India Docks, London. This example of Fowler's Derby handiwork survived well into BR days, not being withdrawn until 1963.

S&D 2-8-0 No. 83, here on loan to the MR in 1919, on up freight near the Welsh Harp.
R.S. Carpenter Collection

Now numbered in the LMS system, the ex-S&D 2-8-0 No. 9678 is one of the batch of five built in 1925 by Stephenson's. In early days these five had large boilers which gradually became interchanged with the small boiler of the 1914 batch.   *R.S. Carpenter Collection*

Extensive trials with the two prototype 0-6-0s were being undertaken in the years leading up to World War I, in addition to several studies for what were to be rather large locomotives by MR standards. There was a need for a powerful freight type to haul heavy goods trains over the steep gradients of the Somerset and Dorset Joint Railway (S&D), which since 1875 had been administered and run by the MR and the London & South Western Railway (LSWR) jointly. Also, there was a pressing need for a powerful banking type to serve the 1 in 37 Lickey incline between Bromsgrove and Blackwell on the MR line from Birmingham to Bristol.

The S&D locomotive was to be a 2-8-0, considerably larger than any type so far built at Derby. By the time the study was well under way, Anderson had given up his chief locomotive draughtsman's position, as he needed to concentrate fully on his Works Manager, or Works Assistant as it was now called, responsibilities. His small engine thinking was therefore removed from the design office. However, the die was cast with his strong views impressed on the senior staff who seemed determined to follow his precepts.

The new chief locomotive draughtsman was Sanford John Symes, who had served an apprenticeship at Inchicore works of the GS&WR in Dublin, becoming a draughtsman there after finishing his time. By 1903 he had progressed to the position of being in charge of the erection of new engines at those works. He then left Inchicore to gain further experience in the design offices of the North British Locomotive Company (NBL) at its Glasgow works. After a few months with the NBL he obtained a position with the MR at Derby as a draughtsman in the LDO, where he was quickly singled out for promotion and proceeded to work his way up through the ranks to chief assistant to Anderson.

The job of the 2-8-0 was given to James Clayton, who started with some schemes for an outside-cylindered 0-8-0 for the S&D proposed under Deeley in 1907. Clayton had hoped to be given Anderson's job, as he was equal in status to Symes. He appears to have been given quite a free hand in his design task, for apart from the size, the 2-8-0 had many features not standard practice at Derby. In particular the outside Walschaerts valve gear was a complete departure from current practice, as was the employment of outside admission valves. The resulting locomotive was a functional design, with one particular bad feature, not the fault of Clayton it should be stated, this being the employment of the class '4F' axleboxes, which proved to be troublesome throughout the life of the engines. Whilst satisfactory as regards static axle loads, these boxes were not adequate to cope with the high tractive effort encountered in service. Hot boxes were to be a continual worry. Other designs to emanate from the Derby LDO in the future were also to be afflicted by the insistence on the employment of this 4F box, as we shall see.

Clayton was not to see the first batch of six into service in 1914, for by then he had left to become chief locomotive draughtsman under Richard Maunsell at the Ashford works of the South Eastern & Chatham Railway (SE&CR). Maunsell was building up a new team for the development of new locomotive stock on that railway. Ashford's gain was Derby's loss, for Clayton was a

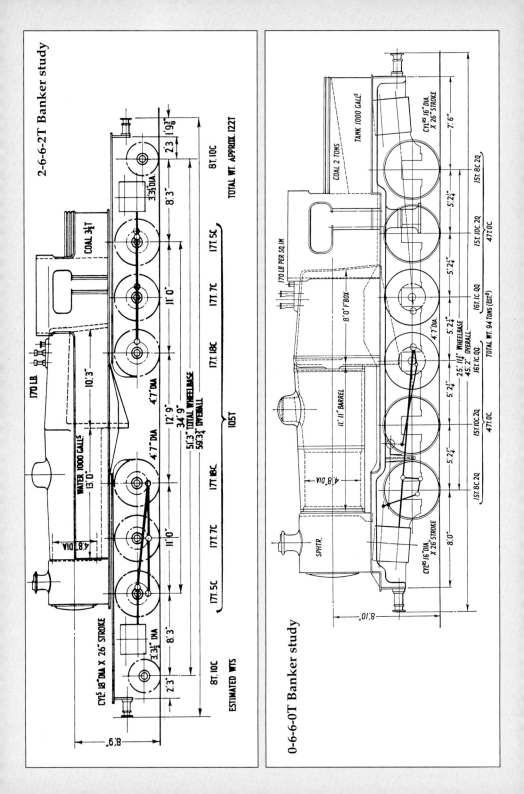

2-6-6-2T Banker study

0-6-6-0T Banker study

talented designer most amenable to the introduction of new ideas. There was to be spasmodic, but important, liaison between Ashford and Derby in the future, in which he would play a significant part. Fowler and Maunsell were, we have seen, old colleagues from their Horwich days and it has been speculated that Clayton's move was the result of Henry realising his natural disappointment that might be evident following Symes' promotion, and that the new opportunity at Ashford might be appropriate to Clayton's obvious talents. Here we see a parallel with Aspinall's handling of promising personnel, in that Henry's own move to the MR had occurred in rather a similar manner.

Up to now banking on the Lickey incline often involved two, or sometimes more, locomotives, not an economic way to employ motive power. A large, powerful, type was needed and Fowler ordered Symes to get the LDO drafting some project studies to satisfy this pressing need.

The Lickey banker studies that emerged were certainly wide-ranging in their layouts, the first one being for a 2-10-0 side tank, the second for an articulated 2-6-6-2 tank, the third for a rigid framed 0-6-6-0 tank, and the fourth and final offering, an 0-10-0 tender type. Table One lists the major design features of the four studies, of which the more conventional 0-10-0 tender type was eventually to be selected for construction. But before anything could be started in the works, political events in Europe stirred up rumours of war, the outbreak of which was to hold up the chosen design's introduction, which appeared on the horizon to threaten the stable order of things.

Table One - The Lickey Banker Studies

Proposal No.	1	2	3	4
Type	2-10-0T	2-6-6-2T	0-6-6-0T	0-10-0
Wheels	4 ft 7 in.	4 ft 7 in.	4 ft 7in.	4 ft 7½in.
No. of cylinders	2	4	4	4
Cylinder diameter/stroke (in.)	21/26	18/26	18/26	16¾/28
Boiler pressure (psi)	200	170	170	180
Superheated	No	Yes	Yes	Yes
Heating surface (sq. ft)	1,523	1,555	1,523	1,718.25
Superheater (sq. ft)	-	-	-	445
Grate area (sq. ft)	25	32	25	31.5
Weight	90.5 t.	122 t.	94 t.	105 t. 4 cwt

With the results of the '4F' trials on the effects of superheating, Henry prepared a paper on this subject for presentation at the Institute of Civil Engineers, and duly gave this to an interested audience. This paper was something of a milestone in the development of that technology. It was delivered on the 13th January and comprehensively covered the many aspects likely to be affected, metallic, lubrication, cylinder design, valve design and maintenance effects. Anderson and Symes were noted as having contributed to the paper. As with many keynote presentations at the I.Civil E. there was a further meeting (two in fact) to allow those who had attended the chance to comment and put their views forward, so on the 20th and 27th January, Henry Fowler listened to and commented on lengthy contributions from Bowen-Cooke, Hill, Raven, J.W. Smith, Gresley and F.H. Trevithick plus many more

Class '483' 4-4-0 No. 419 as rebuilt by Fowler in 1913 on a stopping passenger train at Trent in 1930.   *R.S. Carpenter Collection*

Two class '483' rebuilds went to the SDJR in 1914, Nos. 70 and 71. Here No. 71 rests at Bournemouth Branksome shed between duties in 1928.   *H.F. Wheeller Collection*

outside the railway scene. Some written contributions were also received later, from as far afield as the USA. The Proceedings of the I.Civil E. devoted no fewer than 167 pages to the paper and its deliberations.

Also in 1914, the Irish arm of the MR, the NCC, needed to supplement its fleet of express locomotives, and the Locomotive Superintendent of that line, Bowman Malcolm, prepared a design for a new 4-4-0, of which a batch of two were built at Derby. These were the first engines to employ superheating on the NCC. Up to now, compounds had reigned supreme, Malcolm having stayed with the Worsdell-von Borries two-cylinder concept since 1890. With superheating now commonplace and giving equivalent economic benefits, the compounds were to be eclipsed on the NCC. The two locomotives were delivered just before the outbreak of war.

Derby works was, we have seen, not producing much in the way of new locomotives at this time, in fact, only the six S&D 2-8-0s, the two NCC 4-4-0s and the two prototype '4F' 0-6-0s were produced since Fowler took office in 1910 and the onset of war. The works were, however, very busy in rebuilding exercises during that time. The major rebuild was that of the class '483' 4-4-0s, of which some 165 were to be dealt with. The rebuild appears to be listed thus more for accountancy purposes, as the resulting engines, with new frames, cylinders and boilers were virtually new throughout. One of Henry Fowler's fads, bogie brakes, appeared on all these rebuilds as well as being retrofitted to many other suitable classes as they came in for overhaul.

The boiler shop was kept busy during these years with new boilers for the 4-4-0s and sundry others for the NCC and LT&SR, plus much repair work and, of course, the production of spares.

Easter 1914 was spent in Germany with Emma. Leaving the children in the capable care of the staff at 'The Homestead' they caught the train to London. From here they travelled via Dover to Ostend and then by overnight train to Cologne, where they arrived at 5.40 am to change trains for Hanover, the ultimate destination. There was sufficient time between the trains for them to explore the city after a breakfast in the station restaurant. Henry made for the cathedral: '. . . which is quite close to the station and is one of the largest churches in existance . . .' he wrote to his Bible Class. 'The church has been completed for some time now and the interior is especially fine. We went inside and found a service was just finishing'.

Following this brief foray into the city, they returned to the station to leave on the 7.20 am for Hanover. As they crossed the road / rail bridge over the Rhine, Henry noticed another bridge consisting of a wooden roadway laid over a number of anchored boats, some of which would be swung away when a boat needed to pass. The train journey took them through the industrial Ruhr and its coalfields, which were all too soon to be engaged in producing weapons of war to feed the German armed forces in the conflict which broke out later that year.

Hanover; 'A very flat town with some fine old brick houses but not a very interesting town taking it altogether' was to be their base for the following five days, staying at the Hotel Bristol centrally located near the station. The day before Good Friday found them visiting the nearby town of Hildesheim: 'with its wonderful half-timbered houses and its 1,000 year old rose tree (which we did not see)', before returning to Hanover in time for lunch, followed by, for Henry, a visit to the local railway works. The link with England and this part of Germany was visible on some of the old buildings in the common use of the Lion and Unicorn on many of the coats of arms displayed. After spending the Easter weekend in Hanover, during which the weather was somwhat damp, Emma and Henry returned to Spondon and the children on the 14th April.

As 1914 moved on, the threat of war appeared on the horizon and the railways were readied for Government control if and when this happened. Production of new locomotives slowed to a trickle as the works were prepared for a switch to armaments. On 4th August, war was declared and shortly afterwards the railways in England, Scotland and Wales came under the control of the Railway Executive Committee. The final batch of class '483' rebuilds was immediately put on hold for the duration, and Derby works was, under Anderson, to change to an important rôle as a producer of munitions. The LDO was kept busy with design matters associated with the new products, and repair schemes for such locomotives as were able to be shopped.

Henry Fowler, still very much involved in his technical societies, was elected as President of the Institution of Locomotive Engineers yet again for 1914, as he was for a further term as President of the University of Birmingham Engineering Society. He awaited developments as the war got under way and Derby began to produce its munitions.

The ARLE involvements continued for Henry, who had been elected Secretary of that body the previous November. His 1914 involvement was notable for the proposal for a standard method for the calculation of locomotive heating surfaces. Considerable discussion on this matter took place at the summer meeting, culminating in a committee comprising of Bowen Cooke, Fowler (of course!), Gresley and Hughes being appointed to report back on this matter. They quite speedily came to agree a method which was proposed thus:

Firebox: Outside (wet side) of firebox to top of foundation ring. Deduct the sectional area to the wetted side of the ring or flanged plate as the case may be - section to be taken close up to the inner firebox plate.
Deduct areas of tube holes.
If any water tubes, surface to be taken on the inside.
No allowance for copper stays or roof stays.
Tubes: Outside surface (wet side) between tube plates.
Calculate on uniform tube diameter.
Elements of superheaters: Inside surface (steam side)
Element begins and ends at smokebox end of large flue tube.
Smokebox tubeplate: No allowance for this.

A little diversion occurred just after the outbreak of war, this being the episode involving John Aspinall, Fowler's old mentor on the L&YR, who was now General Manager of that railway. Aspinall was on holiday in Germany, at Bad Homburg, stubbornly believing that the politicians would back down at the last minute and he could safely stay the time he had planned. However, by the time he realised this was not a sensible attitude, civilian travel by rail had been banned by the German Government. He managed to get his wife safely away, but he himself was interned and sent to Munsterlager camp. Considerable diplomatic pressure was put through the office of the Secretary of State for Foreign Affairs by the L&YR, which eventually resulted in Aspinall's release and repatriation at the end of September. Henry Fowler, along with other railway colleagues wrote to Aspinall congratulating him on his safe return and especially thanking him for positive news brought back of one of the other prisoners, the husband of a Mrs Knapp from Spondon: 'You have not only brought yourself back but the news you have brought with regards to prisoners must have relieved great anxiety in many cases. We have one in our village of Spondon where Mrs Knapp is a different woman since she heard of her husband through you'.

As soon as it was obvious the war was going to continue for some time, Harry, the eldest son, decided to leave Oundle a year early, at the age of 17, to enlist in the Army. Henry and Emma must have had some misgivings as to the wisdom of this, but Harry was adamant, he wished to serve his King and Country. He joined the Royal Engineers and soon acquired a commission, being posted to France shortly after his basic training was completed. His decision was to colour the rest of his life quite dramatically, as we shall see shortly.

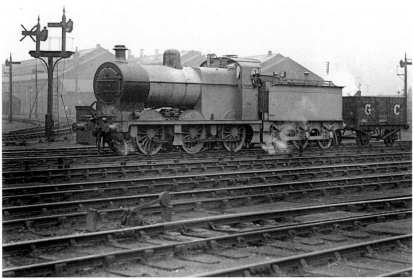

The '4F' class 0-6-0, to become the largest class designed under Fowler. No. 3910, built in 1919, seen here in undercoat during running in around Derby. *R.S. Carpenter Collection*

'The Derby Ram'

Up-to-date

As I was going to Derby, Sir, all on a summer's day,
I met the finest ram, Sir, that ever was fed on hay.

Chorus
And indeed, Sir, 'tis true, Sir, I never were given to lie;
And if you'd been to Derby, Sir, you'd have seen him as well as I.

This ram was fat behind, Sir, this ram was fat before;
This ram was ten feet high, Sir, be sure he was no more. - *Chorus*

The tail was fifty yards, Sir, near as I can tell,
And it was sent to Spondon to ring St Werburgh's bell. - *Chorus*

The wool from off his back, Sir, was fifty packs and ten,
They made it into socks, Sir, for our gallant fighting men. - *Chorus*

And after that was left, Sir, a few packs, six or seven,
From which they made the trousers for the Spondon first eleven. - *Chorus*

The hide became good leather, which cut both thick and thin,
And used for boots for British troops who're marching to Berlin. - *Chorus*

In times past, I have heard, Sir, Derby did her share;
Wherever there was fighting you'd bound to find them there. - *Chorus*

Still Derby men are willing, and want to have a slam,
And the Germans will be sorry when they meet the Derby Ram. - *Chorus*

Additional verses dedicated to the Members of Spondon Bible Class who have joined the Forces.

October, 1914.   *H.F. and H.F.*

Chapter Four

The War Years: I

At the beginning of the war, the British forces were woefully short of armaments. Approximately two machine-guns per battalion, artillery supplied with shrapnel and not high explosive shells, a shortage of heavy guns, mortars, howitzers and the like was the order of the day. The arsenals were still using out-of-date methods of production, such production as was made was falling behind schedule. Something had to be done, and quickly. Lloyd George proposed and, eventually, created the Ministry of Munitions to address this problem, and immediately the race began to find persons with suitable expertise to place into key positions in this organisation.

As the Government grappled with the problem of reorganising the production of munitions, one of Henry's first wartime efforts was an unusual one. In keeping with his wish to maintain contact with those of his team who had felt the call to join up and serve their country, he wrote letters to some of them in the trenches to let them know that their colleagues at home were thinking of them and supporting them in their own way. Many a MR man under fire in the battlefield must have been heartened by the notes sent by their old chief. This practice of encouragement continued, as time permitted, for the rest of the war as did the sending of parcels to the many men from Spondon on active service, organised by Emma and members of Spondon Women's Institute. Many members of Henry's Bible Class had joined up, in fact some 52 were to do so as the war progressed, and were added to the list of encouraging letters. In October 1914, Henry and his eldest son sat down to concoct a new version of the local song 'The Derby Ram' dedicated to the members of the Bible Class who had gone to serve their King and Country. This is printed in full opposite.

It was thus not until June 1915 that Henry Fowler's talents as an organiser were called into Government service with the Ministry of Munitions, a fact which was minuted at the ARLE summer meeting. The job was a daunting one, that of Director of Production, to organise and oversee the production of munitions and all that goes with it, throughout the United Kingdom. Many of the railway workshops were eminently suited for the heavy engineering tasks associated with the production of guns and ammunition, so it was logical to call their expertise and facilities into play. This war was going to be a long one and every square foot of production space was needed. The railways were under Government control for the duration and so there was immediate access to a considerable manufacturing base. Most, if not all, of the railway works were involved in this important task which was in urgent need of co-ordination such that adequate supplies reached the front line as and when needed. Henry Fowler, with his many contacts throughout the railway world and brilliant organisational skills, was in a good position to oversee this task. In one shop of the Derby works the workers, many of them now women, a fair number of men having either been drafted into or voluntarily joined the Forces, were gearing up for the recycling of brass 18-pounder cartridge cases for re-use. A peak

A 1917 photograph of the Derby Works Erecting Shop. Locomotives under repair/construction share the area with these women busily engaged in war work. *Midland Railway Trust*

An aerial view of the Royal Aircraft Factory taken in 1916. This is essentially the facility taken over by Henry Fowler in that year. Just left of centre in this view the whirling arm propeller test gear can be seen. *© (British) Crown Copyright, 1999 Defence Evaluation and Research Agency, reproduced with the permission of the Controller, Her (Britannic) Majesty's Stationary Office*

production rate of some 130,000 per week was eventually reached, with over seven million being dealt with over the years of the war.

In fact, within days of Fowler's commencement of his war service, Bowen Cooke received a request from him to sound out the ARLE members for 50 millwrights to erect shafting and machinery at the BSA company, to expand production facilities at that vital plant.

Although, so far, his locomotive work was not anything of great note, Henry's abilities as an organiser were fully to the fore in this war work. He had the knack of being able to organise many different strands into a cohesive whole, and his capacity for hard work, and long hours of discussion, paid dividends as the Ministry sought to ensure that supplies of munitions and their ancilliaries were forthcoming. In a little over a year matters were running smoothly enough and production levels had soared sufficiently for his talents to be moved elsewhere.

As it was realised that Fowler was likely to be away on war work much of the time, Anderson was delegated to be Deputy CME for the duration, as new design work was virtually at a standstill and he could cope with this extra effort on top of his Works Assistant responsibilities.

The increase in munitions production, following Henry Fowler's appointment, can be graphically shown by referring to two specific examples: In May 1915 the weekly output of shells was just 70,000. By January 1916 this had become over three times as great at 238,000. Similarly, in 1914 a mere 238 machine-guns were manufactured, and by 1916 this had risen to 33,000. The organisational skills were in full play, and Henry saw to it that every available space in the many railway works were used to maximum advantage in the quest for armaments which, as the battles raged to and fro in France, had a frightening wastage rate, continually threatening to outstrip the available supplies. Even the small NCC works at York Road in Belfast was pressed into use, for after building some 70 lorries for the Army in 1915, this facility turned to the output of 4½ inch shells for the remainder of the war years.

The large production increases brought about by Fowler's expertise brought him to the notice of the upper echelons in the Ministry and an event taking place elsewhere was to result in a move to a totally different sphere.

The Royal Aircraft Factory at Farnborough, ostensibly set up as a design and research facility as far back as 1878, although strictly confined to balloons in those early days, was under critical appraisal by the Burbidge Committee, set up in mid-1916 to assess the management of this important plant. Up to now the main production of aircraft designed at the Royal Aircraft Factory was being carried out by private industry, the Royal Aircraft Factory itself having only built some 77 aircraft in total. In view of the obvious pioneering work emanating from this establishment, one of the Committee's recommendations was that it be restructured as a purely research organisation. It also was due for a change of Superintendent and so it was here that Fowler was dispatched. The current incumbent, Lieut Col Mervyn O'Gorman, had reached the end of his seven year contract and did not wish it to be renewed. The Burbidge Committee being aware of this, had recommended that there should be a Board of Management which would comprise an Administration Director,

Johnson 0-4-0ST No. 1515 of this class was sent to the Royal Aircraft Factory on Fowler's orders.
John Scott-Morgan Collection

The RAE railway remained in operation until the mid-1960s. Most of the locomotives were 0-4-0ST types. Here in 1950 No. 7, a Bagnall locomotive, hauls a train through the streets from the main line to the RAE.   *John Scott-Morgan Collection*

Superintendents of Design and Manufacture and a Military Advisor. The Air Board, to whom the report was sent, did not agree with this commercial approach: '. . . however suitable for a private factory, would be ill-adapted to exigencies of military organization'. The Royal Aircraft Factory should, they reasoned, be under the direction of a single Superintendent. This person should be someone with sound management skills and an engineering background but need not necessarily have much knowledge of aeronautics. The Ministry therefore appointed Henry Fowler to this demanding task, and he took office on 21st September, 1916, the first civilian to hold this post.

The site at Farnborough was already very extensive and from the design offices there a range of aircraft designs had emanated for the Royal Flying Corps (RFC). With the private constructors also designing their own aircraft, notably such organisations as the Bristol Aeroplane Company, Sopwith Aviation and Nieuport and General Aircraft, the continuation of the Royal Aircraft Factory designs was a doubtful entity on the grounds that the Royal Aircraft Factory was run by the Ministry that also selected and purchased the aircraft. Hence the need to turn to a purely research centre which could be used by the outside industry.

Some bad feelings were aroused by this policy change and some of the key staff were disheartened, having been established there for some years. Henry's genial nature and quick decision making managed to smooth over some of these people long enough to enable the transition of the 5,000 strong workforce from manufacture to primarily research to be achieved satisfactorily, although some manufacturing did continue in order to relieve the pressure on the already over-loaded private constructors.

The Farnborough site boasted its own standard gauge tramway system, used primarily for the movement of supplies, which was originally totally self-contained. A start had been made to connect this system to the main line. Fowler immediately contacted Herbert Walker, General Manager of the LSWR, and within a few weeks the Royal Aircraft Factory railway connection to the LSWR main line at Farnborough station a short distance away was in operation, to permit the speedy transition of supplies into the site. The work for this connection was carried out, somewhat reluctantly, by prisoners-of-war under the supervision of the Royal Engineers.

Initially, the only locomotive, if it can be classed as such, was a modified Fowler traction engine which, although capable of moving wagons about did so at a snail's pace. So to provide a better source of motive power for this internal railway, Fowler was soon on the telephone to Anderson at Derby and arrangements were made to transfer a Johnson 0-4-0ST, No. 1515, to work the system. This little shunting locomotive was speedily delivered and soon in daily use around the site. Its four-coupled chassis of just 7 ft wheelbase was ideal for the tight curves that abounded.

One interesting project under way when Fowler took office was for a radio-controlled flying bomb postulated by the RFC's Experimental Wing at Feltham, whose commanding officer was Captain A.M. Low. Low's expertise did not run to aircraft design, he was primarily a radio man, and so the Royal Aircraft Factory was contracted to design and build a suitable aircraft. At Farnborough the project was labelled 'Aerial Target' to hide its real purpose. H.P. Folland

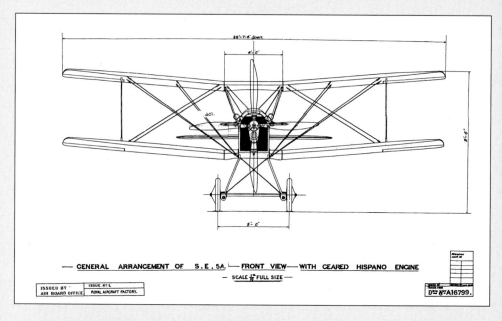

General arrangement drawing of SE5a, front elevation.

General arrangement drawing of SE5a, side elevation.
(Both) © (British) Crown Copyright, 1999 Defence Evaluation and Research Agency, reproduced with the permission of the Controller, Her (Britannic) Majesty's Stationary Office

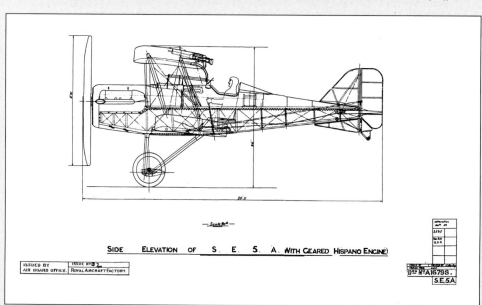

was the designer given the job and a small shoulder-wing monoplane designed. Six examples were built and sent to Feltham to have the radio equipment installed. The initial flight trials were, however, not successful and the project was eventually abandoned. It was resurrected in the 1920s and led eventually to the radio-controlled target aircraft used in limited numbers for gunnery practice by the Royal Navy, thus fulfilling its original, misleading, designation. This early attempt at what we now know as Cruise Missiles goes to show that, often, modern developments are based on an old concept which had been thwarted by the restricted level of technology available in the pioneering days.

In keeping with his wish to make all aware of the happenings at the Royal Aircraft Factory, Henry instigated a regular series of meetings with local officials and organisations to explain to them the changes he planned to make for further expansion of the Royal Aircraft Factory and its eventual rôle as a primary means of aeronautical research. Much of what the factory had been doing was unknown to those living in the vicinity and, as it was a prime employer in that area, Henry thought it was only fair to let those in high places locally know a little about this major contributor to the local economy. These meetings were much appreciated by the authorities in and around Farnborough, particularly as Fowler was the first Superintendent to communicate in such a direct way.

Concurrent to the reorganisation which now commenced was the development of a new fighter aircraft sorely needed by the RFC to combat the German Fokkers and the new Albatros, at that time holding an ascendency over the French and British types then in service.

The aircraft under development at the time of Henry Fowler's appointment, the SE5, was to become a classic amongst the fighters of World War I, being designed by H.P. Folland who was a leading designer at the Factory. The prototype construction started shortly after Henry took his position as Superintendent and by the middle of November had been completed and the engine test runs commenced. A first flight was achieved on the 22nd November. The SE5 had a powerful Hispano-Suiza V-8 water-cooled engine of some 200 bhp, which gave the aircraft a performance equal to anything on the Western Front. It was very rigidly built, capable of dive speeds up to nearly 300 mph, and had well harmonised controls.It was also notable for the fact that it was the first British fighter to employ a trimming tailplane and adjustable pilot's seat, plus a formidable armament of two guns, one firing through the propeller. Fowler, as he settled into his new position, allowed Folland and his team to develop their new aircraft as they saw fit, whilst he concentrated on the reorganisation of the Establishment to a more research oriented facility, coupled with planning for the mass production of the fighter.

In late 1916, King George V paid an official visit to the Royal Aircraft Factory, now in the throes of reorganisation, and was conducted around by Henry Fowler, who was shortly to receive his first honour, the CBE. Henry clearly got on well with the King, and the resulting photograph of the two of them resulted in Queen Mary commenting that this was the first time the King had smiled since the dreadful losses incurred in the Battle of the Somme, in which some 410,000 casualties (60,000 on the first day alone), were listed.

General Arrangement
Drawing of SE5a,
Plan View

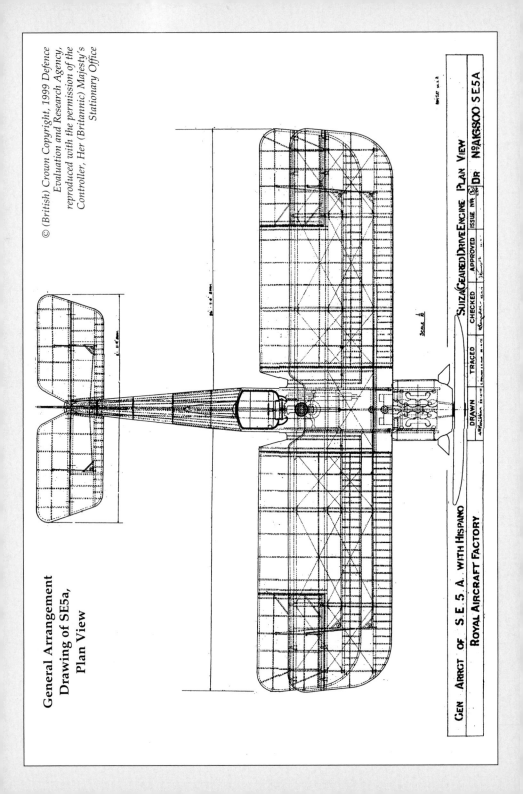

GEN ARRGT OF S.E.5.A. WITH HISPANO SUIZA GEARED DRIVE ENGINE PLAN VIEW

ROYAL AIRCRAFT FACTORY

Above: The prototype SE5 Fighter, with Frank Goodden in the cockpit. This was unarmed and considerable detail differences are visible on the forward part of the fuselage when compared to the production version.
Below: A production SE5a. This is a particularly clear sharp photograph. The aircraft is standing on the circle of concrete used for compass calibrations.
(Both) © (British) Crown Copyright, 1999 Defence Evaluation and Research Agency, reproduced with the permission of the Controller, Her (Britannic) Majesty's Stationary Office

Henry Fowler and King George V at the Royal Aircraft Factory, Farnborough. Henry appears very much at ease and this is the only known photograph to survive showing him in the straw boater so popular with him. The moustache, at that time, was still waxed.
© (British) Crown Copyright, 1999 Defence Evaluation and Research Agency, reproduced with the permission of the Controller, Her (Britannic) Majesty's Stationary Office

Despite his Farnborough committments, Henry Fowler managed to attend the November 1916 ARLE meeting, at which discussion of alternative materials for firebox construction was a major item. Henry was minuted as having stated that he had often found that repairs to copper boxes invariably used more copper than that needed for complete renewal.

Testing of the SE5 continued until 17th January, 1917 when a pre-production model suffered an in-flight port wing failure, the resulting crash killing the pilot Frank Goodden. Fowler immediately convened an investigation into the disaster which initially blamed the propeller for breaking and causing large out-of-balance forces which made the wings flex excessively. However, this did not fit the evidence exactly, so an external investigation by the Military Aeronautics Department was called. This concluded that a design deficiency in the wing structure had allowed the wing to collapse internally. A structural test on the remaining prototype confirmed this and remedial structural modifications made by the design team. By the 1st March the first production batch, now designated as SE5a, was turned out of the Royal Aircraft Factory. Meantime, Folland had resigned his position, taking the blame for the design fault which had cost Goodden his life. He was to end up in the aircraft industry as a major designer, eventually to form his own company which survived into the 1960s, albeit by then taken over in the massive amalgamations of those years. Reports & Memoranda (R&M) No. 491, still available from DERA, gives a good account of the findings associated with the crash, and shows the inadequate safety factor on the upper wing front spar which was remedied by the redesign.

Once the supply of engines for the SE5a from the Wolseley Company had been resolved, the original Hispano-Suiza supply being insufficient, production contracts were placed, where possible, amongst the hard-pressed aircraft manufacturers and elsewhere. Henry Fowler soon had Martynside, Vickers, the Air Navigation Company, Austin Motors, and Wolseley, in addition to the Royal Aircraft Factory itself, setting up production lines. Over the following 15 months of the war that remained 5,205 of the SE5a's were built and issued to 12 squadrons on the Western Front, four Home squadrons and four overseas squadrons in the Middle East plus equipping 11 training squadrons in the UK.

The SE5a in terms of its combat victories ranked as the second most successful of all World War I fighters employed by the RFC, despite only being in service a little over a year. Only the Sopwith Camel exceeded its tally. Many of World War I aces, such as Albert Ball, used the SE5a as their chosen steed. Much havoc was wreaked amongst the Fokkers and Albatroses of the German Air Force. So the progress of the war in the air for the Allies has much to thank Henry Fowler for in his organisation of the mass production of a fine aircraft.

Henry's determination to ensure that a first-class fighter was available for the RFC was increased by the fact that early in the morning of 1st February, 1916, Zeppelin No. L14, after an abortive search for Liverpool, arrived over Derby and loosed 4,150 lb. of high explosive bombs on the city. Many fell on the railway works badly damaging some shops and one of the engine sheds. As the works were virtually empty, only three were killed and two injured. The Zeppelin captain, on his return to Germany, reported as having bombed Nottingham. Little did he know that he had been so close to influencing much damage on the Rolls-Royce plant! From this plant and the designs which it produced was to come some 60 per cent of the power employed in the air by the Allies during the whole of the war.

Emma and the children may well have heard the drone of the Zeppelin's engines high above and the explosions in Derby just a couple of miles away from Spondon.

Henry was well pleased with the outcome of the SE5a episode, and in what spare moments were available, took a passing interest in problems associated with air-cooled aero engines then being developed at the Royal Aircraft Factory. Also, the foundations were laid for Derby works to carry out some manufacturing work for Farnborough, notably forged flywheels and also aluminium high compression pistons to reduce the weight of aero engines.

In fact, to remain on the aircraft side of things, Derby works was responsible for the production of some 4,500 aircraft during the war.

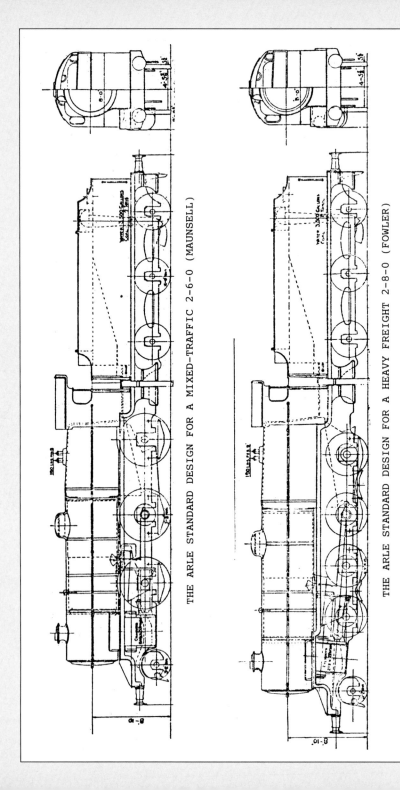

THE ARLE STANDARD DESIGN FOR A MIXED-TRAFFIC 2-6-0 (MAUNSELL)

THE ARLE STANDARD DESIGN FOR A HEAVY FREIGHT 2-8-0 (FOWLER)

G. Hughes

ARLE 2-6-0 and 2-8-0 studies

Chapter Five

The War Years: II

Still Secretary of the ARLE during the war years, Fowler managed to attend the two 1917 meetings. At the summer gathering he seconded Hill's (GER) proposal for an 80 per cent factor on boiler pressure to be used for the calculation of tractive effort. No vote was taken and the proposal drifted off the agenda. The November meeting is the first one at which some of the ARLE 'standard' locomotives were discussed. A designing committee was appointed to cover two specific types: a 2-6-0 for mixed traffic with Maunsell being given overall charge, and a 2-8-0 for freight use under Fowler.

By the end of 1917, his efforts for the Ministry of Munitions and the Farnborough Superintendency were rewarded by the award of the CBE. He also was given even greater responsibility at this time, being made Assistant Director General of Aircraft Production on top of his Superintendency at the Royal Aircraft Factory. The SE5a episode had clearly been noted and in February 1918 he was ordered to attend an investiture at Buckingham Palace. Here he was rewarded for his services to the munitions industry, and aviation in particular, by a justly deserved knighthood and the honorary rank of Lieutenant-Colonel in the RFC. This took place on 20th February, 1918, with Sir Henry noting in one of his letters to Bible Class members in the Front Line: 'The King struck me on both shoulders. I got a silver star to wear on my left breast, as well as the Order [this being Knight Commander of the Order of the British Empire] to wear round my neck'. The knighthood was not the first in the Fowler family, for as far back as the time of Richard I one Richard Fowler was in the English camp at the seige of Ascalon during the Crusades. One night he was awakened by the hooting of an owl and noticed some suspicious movements of a raiding party about to attack the camp. He alerted the King and other officers and the raiders were surprised and driven off. For this he was knighted in the field by the King. The second record of such an honour belongs to Sir John Fowler of ploughing machine fame, as recounted in Chapter One.

Sir Henry's meetings with the King continued, in between trips to Paris on Ministry business, and one such event is described by him with evident relish:

Some of you have, I believe, seen an account of my going to Lincoln with the King and Queen, but as some may not have done so I will tell you shortly. On the way there I met an American Captain. The following day I found out that he could be presented to the King, and after a big push I got hold of him. I presented him and his Sergeant to the King and Queen, and he at once whipped out an envelope and asked the Queen to sign it. This she did on the Sergeant's back, and he then asked the King to do so. The King said 'What am I to sign on?', and so I said 'Have my back, Sir'. He did so, but the American's pen would not work, and so I whipped mine out of my pocket and said 'Try an English one, Sir'. It was great and the American Captain was very set up. The papers had it all in.

In March 1918 came another move, this time to the full-time post of Deputy Director-General of Aircraft Production. However, it is worth pointing out here that the legacy Henry Fowler gave to aviation was the fact that he laid the foundation for what became the Royal Aircraft Establishment, as the Royal Aircraft Factory became known as from mid 1918, which prospers to this day as the DERA and is still a major World leader in aerospace research, from which has come much of the theoretical and practical knowledge resulting in the only operational supersonic airliner the World has yet seen, the Anglo-French Concorde.

Coupled to the Deputy Director-General's post were some administrative appointments connected to aviation, these being the Ministry of Munitions' representative on the Aircraft Mission to the United States and Canada of 1918, Chairman of the First Allied Conference on the Standardisation of Aircraft Components, and membership of the Advisory Committee for Aeronautics, eventually to become the Aeronautical Research Council, where his metallurgical expertise was called into play as Chairman of the light alloys sub-committee. Finally, so far as the Ministry was concerned, he was elected a Member of the Munitions Council.

This most certainly was a very full agenda, with the trip to America taking place in June 1918. Yet, still on top of all this he did manage to find some time to be involved in the ARLE locomotive design committee, which was increasingly involved in the preparation of a series of designs for standard locomotives. These were to be considered for mass production should the post-war plans of the Government result in a Nationalised railway network. All the indications were, once the country moved towards a cessation of hostilities, that State ownership of a merged network was a serious prospect for the railway system, which clearly needed some reform following the effects of wartime inflation and the general lack of routine maintenance on stock, track and equipment with the railway works largely involved in war work.

The ARLE meetings, however, were largely delegated to Anderson in his capacity as Acting CME, who took little notice of arguments forcefully put forward by Churchward, a regular attender, for long travel, long lap valves on all the designs covered by this group. Maunsell on the SE&CR, who was CME of this group, had already adopted this principle on his current designs, a 2-6-0 mixed traffic and 2-6-4T passenger tank locomotives. Prototypes of both were in service and proving excellent engines, whilst series production awaited the end of hostilities when the railway works could get back to large-scale production. The MR, with Fowler being briefed by Anderson, still clung to short travel valves and there were, apparantly, long arguments between Fowler and Maunsell on such matters on the few occasions that they met. However, the long travel, long lap, concept was not completely to escape the MR, or LMS as it was to become, as we shall see later on.

Evidence from the minutes of the ARLE meetings has produced the fact that there were supposed to be many common features between the 2-6-0 (Ashford) and 2-8-0 (Derby) designs, in particular the cylinders, piston valves, motion and valve gear. Here is evidence that the Derby LDO *must* have considered long travel, long lap valve gears if complete commonality was to be adhered to, for the Maunsell derived 2-6-0 was a large-boilered version of his SE&CR prototype that embodied such gear. Had the Nationalisation scheme been adopted and the standard designs built by the relevant design centres, it would have been interesting to see how the Derby design would have finally emerged, if it had been chosen. Table Two, below, summarises the particulars of the proposed locomotives.

Table Two - Proposed Standard Locomotives

Type		2-8-0	2-6-0
Driving wheels diameter		4 ft 8 in.	5ft 8 in.
Piston valve diameter		10 in.	10 in.
Valve Gear		Walschaerts	Walschaerts
Bissel truck wheels dia		3 ft 2 in.	3 ft 2 in.
Frames		1⅛ in.	1¼ in.
Boiler outside dia		5 ft 6 in.	5 ft 6 in.
Distance between tubeplates		14 ft 5⅝ in.	12 ft 6⅝ in.
Working pressure		180 lb./sq. in	180 lb./sq. in
Grate area		30 sq. ft	25sq. ft
Flues		24 x 5¼ in.	24 x 5¼ in.
Tubes		166 x 1⅞ in.	166 x 1⅞ in.
Superheater (Robinson)		24 x 1⅜ in.	24 x 1⅜ in.
Heating surface, firebox		158 sq. ft.	135sq ft.
	tubes	1643.8 sq. ft	1,433 sq. ft
	superheater	268 sq. ft	254 sq. ft
Cylinders (2)	Diameter	21½ in.	20½ in.
	Stroke	28 in.	28 in.
Chimney height from rails		13 ft	13 ft
Maximum axle load		17 t. 12 cwt	19 t. 0 cwt
Total wt, engine & tender		119 t.	109 t.
Tractive Effort		33,282 lb.	24,919 lb.

Top feed, steel firebox, Ross pop valves,
Injectors, right Davies and Metcalfe exhaust steam injector
Injectors, left   Gresham and Craven live steam injector

Sir Henry continued in Government service for some months following the Armistice, signed on the 11th November, 1918. There was much to be done in the switch back to peacetime production rates for munitions. The railway works could fairly easily slip back into their peacetime rôles of building, servicing and maintaining their stock. With the big specialised concerns such as Woolwich Arsenal it was a different matter, their life-blood had gone with the onset of peace and several plans were implemented to attempt to allay the large layoffs. Sir Henry gradually handed over his Ministerial responsibilities to those of the permanent staff who had faithfully assisted his tasks, after which he returned to his old post at Derby, to pick up the reins in the CME's office. Anderson relinquished his temporary CME post, but his influence in the LDO was to remain for some time, as we will see. Sir Henry's initial salary upon his return of £3,000 was much improved over his pre-war remuneration and was, in a few months, to rise to £3,500.

Fowler had, in 1918, been elected to the Council of the I.Mech.E., so the round of meetings at this Institution were set to continue after the war had finished. Also, at the November 1918 ARLE meeting, the value of percentage boiler pressure to be used in the Phillipson formula was raised again by Sir Henry. He had obviously forgotten that just two years previously the ARLE had suggested the value of 80 per cent. This gave Gresley the opportunity to press for 85 per cent, which he had long suggested. A vote was taken and Gresley's suggestion passed to become a standard for the future.

Some limited production of the '4F' 0-6-0 had been undertaken during the war years, with 15 outshopped in 1917, two more batches of 10 each in 1918, plus authorisation for a further 15 as war ended. There was a shortfall in 0-6-0 goods locomotives caused by the transfer of 81 Kirtley types to the Railway Operating Division (ROD), of which 61 were dispatched overseas, and this had prompted the production of the extra '4Fs'.

The ROD was under the command of Cecil Paget, who had joined up early in the war and sensibly the War Office placed him where his railway background would be at a distinct advantage. Paget had considerable dealings with Richard Maunsell, as Ashford works took responsibility for servicing ROD locomotives and stock as regards spare parts. Ashford was ideally placed, being near the Channel ports, and Maunsell frequently visited France to liaise with Paget on such matters. Many of the types pressed into service in France came from Belgium, completely over-run by the German forces and so it was necessary to manufacture such spare parts as were needed by reference to the actual items, The Ashford design office was kept busy on this work for some time, and Paget acknowledged his debt to Maunsell for the smoothing over of red tape associated with such work in a note written at the end of the war.

Meantime, the Paget experimental locomotive still sat in a remote corner of Derby works. One of the early decisions taken by Fowler on his return was to have this failure cut up for scrap. Space in the tight confines of Derby works was at a premium, now that plans for considerable new construction in the near future could be foreseen.

The efforts as Deputy Director-General of Aircraft Production, on top of the previous work as Director of Production were so appreciated by the Government of the day that Sir Henry Fowler was recommended for a Peerage. The authorities even went as far as having a coat of arms drafted by the College of Arms. This coat of arms was unique, in that it incorporated the form of an aeroplane, the first time such a symbol had been used in such a manner. Sir Henry, whilst immensely flattered by this great honour, graciously declined the offer as it was a hereditary title which meant that the title and the majority of his assets would pass to the eldest son, with the other children receiving short shrift. He preferred to stay with just the knighthood and be in a position to divide his wealth equally between the children and Lady Emma in the event of his death.

To close this chapter on the war episodes, out of the 52 Spondon Bible Class members on active service, 47 returned safely to Spondon at the close of the war, albeit with some of them somewhat the worse for their experiences, particularly Sir Henry's eldest son, Harry. They had been faithfully fed with information and supplies from home, the former by Sir Henry's regular letters, and the latter from the unofficial committee of members of the Women's Institute, led by Emma Fowler, attached to St Werburgh's Church in Spondon, both of which most certainly kept their spirits up during that most exhausting and bloody war.

Chapter Six

The Return to the Midland Railway

It was not until May 1919 that Henry could return to his CME position. Anderson stepping down from Acting CME and returning to the Works Assistant rôle on a full-time basis. There was not much to report on the production front so far as locomotives were concerned, with only 50 examples of the '4F' 0-6-0 being constructed in 1917-19. Therefore his first priority was to set to and assess where the main thrust of design work was to be concentrated. There was the outstanding requirement for the banking engine to assist traffic up the 1 in 37½ Lickey incline between Bromsgrove and Blackwell, the subject of several project studies (detailed in Chapter Three) which had been terminated when war broke out from which had been chosen the 0-10-0 tender design. It was not until Fowler returned to Derby that the order for a single example was placed. For a railway with a small engine policy, the resulting locomotive was the largest ever produced by the MR and unique in the fact that it was the only tender example of this wheel arrangement to appear in the UK. (There was, of course, Holden's 0-10-0T of 1903 on the Great Eastern Railway, which only spent a short time in service before being withdrawn and, eventually, rebuilt as an 0-8-0 tender engine).

Accordingly, December 1919, saw the rolling out of this leviathan from Derby works. With its four cylinders of 16¾ inch diameter and 28 inch stroke fed by a boiler having a total heating surface of 2163.25 sq. ft. and pressure of 180 lb. per sq.in. the tractive effort was a massive 44,030 lb. It went straight into service on the Lickey incline, where it was to stay the majority of its life, only being withdrawn in 1956, as the end of steam approached on BR.

Also, in May 1919, the ARLE convened a special conference at the Midland Grand Hotel to consider a memorandum from Fowler on specifications for steels, an earlier discussion on firebox materials having awakened his metallurgical interests.

The MR Locomotive Drawing Office, which had slimmed down slightly during the war, was being built up again in preparation for a big design programme, although rumours of reorganisation of the railways were beginning to be heard from political sources. The technical staff in the LDO consisted of 11 senior draughtsmen, 6 junior draughtsmen, 4 assistants (mainly ex-servicemen with draughting experience), 2 tracers, a clerk and an office boy. The staff still arrived by train, tram or cycle and braved the elements on the bridge and/or open staircase that led to the second floor on which was the LDO. The private car was still an item of the future for all but the privileged few. At this time the only persons to arrive by car were Sir Henry and S.J. Symes, whose steeds were garaged (and maintained) by those responsible for such motor transport as was used by the MR in the Works Trucks department.

Although Anderson had reverted to the Works Assistant post, he still had a strong influence over the LDO via S.J. Symes who had, as recorded earlier, succeeded him as chief draughtsman. We have seen that for nearly four years prior to this Anderson had been Acting CME and his influence had only been removed on Fowler's return. The change back to Fowler's way of thinking

The Lickey banker, No. 2290 awaits its next turn of duty at Blackwell in 1920.
R.S. Carpenter Collection

World War I resulted in a shortage of locomotives, and shortly after the cessation of hostilities, many passenger types could be found pressed into other service. Here '483' class No. 426 waits at Blackwell to descend the Lickey Bank with a lengthy freight.   *R.S. Carpenter Collection*

must have been a problem for Symes, for he was well steeped in Anderson's ways by now.

His continued lack of close contact with the LDO ordinary staff made Fowler's ideas amenable to subtle change by Symes, with sometimes adverse effects on the resulting design task. However, not wishing to upset the boat too much, Sir Henry accepted in the main what was offered via his chief draughtsman. He had plenty of other matters on his hands outside the sphere of Derby works, for shortly after returning to the railway he learnt of his election to the Presidency of the Institution of Automobile Engineers for 1920. He still captained the Spondon cricket team, was now a Governor of the Midland Railway Institute, President of the Derby Hockey Club and continued his Bible classes in Spondon. Additionally, he was busy preparing a further paper on superheating for presentation at the I.Mech.E. in 1922. Life was certainly full outside the busy bustle of Derby works as the 1920s commenced.

On the political side, the Railway Executive Committee were still discussing Nationalisation and at this time were also dealing with the standardisation of brakes. A group of three from the railway scene, Sir Francis Dent, Sir Henry Fowler and Nigel Gresley had been asked to cover this subject, liaising with Continental engineers, to try and see if an international body might be formed. Fowler and Gresley immediately saw an opportunity to collaborate on braking technology, a test programme for which was in action by the end of the year. The continuous automatic brake for passenger trains had now been in existance for 50 years and yet the goods scene was still way behind, in that loose-coupled and unbraked stock still proliferated. Gresley's Great Northern Railway wished to run express goods trains at average speeds of 45 mph and was progressively fitting vans with continuous vacuum brakes and screw couplings. Some trains consisting of up to 101 vehicles of such stock were tested between Peterborough and Spalding to assess the braking efficiencies. The objective of the tests was to obtain emergency stops without parting the trains and also in such a manner that an immediate restart was feasible. Two main difficulties arose from the analysis of the trials, these being the obtaining of a smooth deceleration without increasing the stopping distances plus the time needed to restore the vacuum along the considerable length of the train.

At the 1921 summer meeting of the ARLE, held this year at the Great Western Hotel, Paddington, Fowler and Gresley announced that the braking trials had been carried out and that this enabled a report to be prepared which became the basis for a joint paper given to the Institution of Civil Engineers in 1922. The results of their findings and recommendations constituted quite a step forward in railway brake development in the United Kingdom. Also set up at this summer meeting was a boiler testing committee consisting of Fowler, Gresley, Pickersgill plus a repesentative of the Ministry of Transport. The latter was to cover the eventuality of Government representation should the current Nationalisation plans materialise.

His war service now over, and *Sir* Henry Fowler having returned to the Derby works, the question of a further move of home raised its head. 'The Homestead' was still rented from the Cade family, who now required to sell the property, having settled themselves permanently in the Cheltenham area. Henry and the family left the house in 1919 for Derwent House, Milford, just north of Derby, having refused the Cade's offer of the opportunity for them to

Spondon Bible Class football team, still thriving in the 1926/7 season. Sir Henry proudly gathers his team after they win the Derby Sunday School championship.   *Spondon Historical Society*

St Werburgh's Church, Spondon.   *Author*

purchase the property. However, their happy days at Spondon were missed and, as the MR moved towards Grouping, Henry and Emma started to think about returning to their old haunt. In their first year away Sir Henry had organised a Christmas evening together for the members of the Bible Class. He accordingly sent a printed note to all members inviting them to the Mission hall, or Iron Room, as the corrugated iron hut was known, at 7.30 pm on Monday 22nd December for whist, refreshments and music. Both he and Lady Emma were there to mix again with all those who attended.

Shortly, another imposing property, Spondon Hall, dating from 1780, was to come onto the market and this got the Fowlers planning on returning to Spondon.

The Bible Class was the catalyst for their return to Spondon. Sir Henry was still involved in this organisation, having become its Chairman and mainstay for many years. Its objective was, as from the beginning, to encourage men to be an active part of the Church (in this case St Werburgh's, Spondon). There was also the added attraction of organising sporting activities, of which one was football. The teams from the Spondon Bible Class, initially encouraged and coached by Fowler, played in the Derby Sunday School League until that amalgamated with another youth league in the 1950s.

A further involvement in the local Church affairs presented itself around this time. St Werburgh's had a fine peal of bells, and the opportunity to become a bell-ringer was offered to Sir Henry, and eagerly accepted. Needless to say he quickly got the hang of handling the ropes and, after much practice, found himself elected as Captain.

The large salary increase for Henry, brought about by the double rise shortly after his return from war service, now made him a wealthy man with a title, so it was natural for the Fowlers to upgrade their home to the ultimate country house. The social requirements of the time, although soon to be outmoded, conspired to elevate the type of accomodation expected with the status a title conferred. Therefore, in 1921, the Fowlers moved back to the village and into Spondon Hall, just a few yards from 'The Homestead'. This was to be Henry's and Emma's final home. The Hall had extensive grounds, complete with coach house and stables. It was the grounds with their profusion of trees and shrubs that aroused in Sir Henry an interest in matters horticultural. In later years, as he travelled overseas, he was liable to bring back unusual, and sometimes, exotic plants for installation there to remind him of his time in the country of their origin.

The elder son, Henry, had returned from his war service in a fragile condition, having been severely shell-shocked. His father accordingly arranged for a quiet job on the MR to be made available for him, and made sure that Henry junior was given the opportunity to settle down into civilian life with the minimum of fuss.

The Institution responsibilities continued to grow for Sir Henry. He had been a Council member of the I.Mech.E. since 1918 and in 1922 was elected a Vice-President. The ARLE Presidency also came his way in 1921 and he was re-elected President of the Institution of Automobile Engineers for a second year in 1921. It seemed that everybody was after his presence for high office.

Little towards new locomotive design was done as the MR moved towards the reorganisations to surface as Grouping. There seemed little point in in turning out new schemes until it was known exactly how the future of the

Spondon Hall c. 1870. The proximity of St Werburgh's Church is evident in this old print. The building was substantially unchanged in the Fowler's time.

Mrs D. Fowler

Above: 'The Homestead' *c.* 1920. Perhaps the building work going on in front of the house decided the Fowlers not to purchase. The ensuing development would most certainly have spoilt the view.
J.R. Hughes/Spondon Historical Society

Left: The coach house, Spondon Hall, in a rather dilapidated condition just before demolition.
J.R. Hughes/Spondon Historical Society

railways in the UK was to be aligned. The only locomotive in large-scale production at Derby was the '4F' 0-6-0, of which 75 were produced, in 1921-2, plus a further 55 contracted out to Armstrong Whitworth. The works still needed some reorganising from its wartime rôle.

The drawing procedure in the LDO was little changed from the pre-war days. The draughtsmen used a special paper with a cloth backing which was dampened and pinned to the board to stretch it flat. The schemes under consideration were drafted onto ordinary paper before transferring them to the board. These sketches were then disposed of into the waste-paper bin. When finished the drawing would be checked for dimensional accuracy by the leading hand and then the approved scheme, still attached to the board, would go to the tracers who copied it onto tracing cloth. When traced the the cloth copy would be signed, usually by the chief draughtsman before being sent to the Photographic department for copying and storing. From here copies would be issued back to the LDO for reference and the shops for production. The main office copies were still coloured up, a quite lengthy job and, in fact, even during the war, this procedure was rigidly followed on munitions work despite the urgency. Method and procedure in the LDO was very important in those days. As regards office staff having access to Fowler himself, one had to have a cast-iron reason to get past his clerk G.J. Pratt, and then at a strictly specified time, more often than not outside normal working hours!

To keep the LDO fully occupied, Fowler applied himself to considering detail design of standard components, one of the first of which was to alter the MR boiler fitting which comprised the combined steam valve and clack box to a lighter version. The resulting item became standard until Stanier took over some 12 years later. Sundry items which tended to vary greatly between locomotive types, such as sanding and blower valves were also standardised to reduce spares holdings and cheapen production costs.

In keeping with many other railways the MR continued to dispatch key people to the USA on fact-finding trips, and Anderson duly departed in 1920, returning with sundry ideas which were schemed but not fully implemented.

The Year 1920 brought a brief apprenticeship at Derby works for none other than Graham Sutherland, the artist in later years, who as a 16-year-old spent a year manfully struggling with eight hours a day in the works building or servicing locomotives followed by evenings of study at the Municipal Technical College. Sutherland's grasp of mathematics, or rather the lack of it, came to the attention of Sir Henry who kindly suggested that he discontinue the apprenticeship and try something else - a procedure young Graham gladly accepted, for the benefit not only of himself, but for the Nation in the future in the form of some great paintings.

The following year brought the first Coal Strike with the promise of more in the future. With the large inflationary pressures caused by the war, many Unions were on the warpath to obtain better wages for their members. Fowler had for some time been interested in the possibilities of oil firing of locomotives and here was something needing a bit of research. He accordingly leapt into action and ordered that some schemes for converting some of the existing goods and passenger fleet to oil firing be looked into as a matter of urgency. The LDO was kept busy as the threat of a prolonged coal shortage hovered on the

Yet another class '483', this time converted for oil burning in 1921 in what looks like ex-works condition.   *JSM Collection*

horizon. Even though the strike was settled reasonably quickly, the work involved was not wasted, for firstly, Fowler was looking for a suitable subject to present in a paper to the next International Railway Congress to be held in Rome in 1922 and, secondly, Richard Maunsell on the SE&CR was looking around for some oil firing methods to try out on that line. He duly liaised with Henry Fowler on this and experimented with the Derby method at Ashford. Henry did not leave matters after the panic had died down, but retained an interest in this form of fuel for some time. His research was to come to the fore in a larger way during the 1926 General Strike.

And so, between 18th April and 3rd May, 1922, the International Railway Congress met in Rome for its Ninth Session. The MR delegation of 10 contained all the top managers, of which Fowler and Reid both presented papers. Sir Henry's was based on his previous years research programme into the oil firing conversions.

The only really serious project on the drawing board around this time was for a mixed-traffic 2-6-0, which was based on the specification for the ARLE standard design study for that wheel arrangement. However, this particular Derby design differed in many respects from that of the ARLE as it was derived from the S&D 2-8-0 being shortened to a 2-6-0, complete with short travel valve gear. However, this was as far as it got, being overtaken by Grouping, and died on the board, the 2-6-0 design that was finally adopted after Grouping coming from Hughes' team at Horwich.

The LT&S arm of the MR requested some studies involving two 0-6-0 freight locomotives whose boilers were worn out, but the rest of the components were in reasonable shape mechanically and worth saving. These two had been built by Beyer, Peacock for Turkey and had been picked up cheaply by the LT&S many years before. Some diagrams utilising the standard Derby 'G5½' boiler on them were prepared. But whether the rebuild actually took place has not been traced.

The MR's Irish arm, the NCC, still retained much of its locomotive developments in-house, although since the absorption of that line in 1903 certain Midland items had been gradually introduced after its long association

One of the two 4-4-0s built at Derby for the NCC in 1922 in as built condition. No. 73, caught at Derry 7th July 1935.   *J.M. Jarvis*

NCC 0-6-0 No. 14, of the 1923 batch, still going strong at Belfast, York Road on 13th June, 1953. Note the Fowler chimney.   *R.G. Jarvis Collection, MRT*

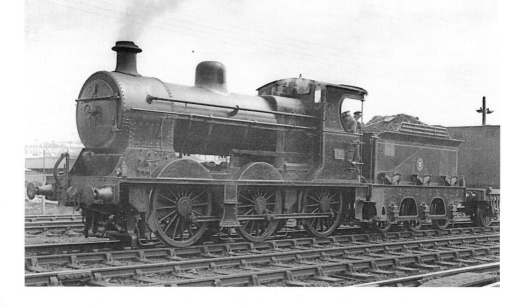

with Beyer, Peacock had been broken at the take-over. There was a need for a pair of 4-4-0s for passenger work and three 0-6-0s for goods work in 1921. The current CME of the NCC, Bowman Malcolm, prepared specifications based on his earlier designs, the superheated class 'U' 4-4-0 of 1914 and his 0-6-0 of 1890. Both were to be simple expansion types. Malcolm had almost exclusively built compounds until the 1914 design and, in fact, Derby had built two of them in 1905. The York Road, Belfast, works of the NCC, whilst capable of building small batches, was really geared up for rebuilds and heavy maintenance.

Derby also wished to exercise more influence towards the stock of this hitherto profitable Irish extension, so here was an opportunity to put this policy into place. Malcolm was approaching retirement after a mammoth career as CME (since 1876) and, in fact, had gone when the five 'new' locomotives were delivered.

Fowler permitted the continued production of, admittedly, obsolescent designs to satisfy the need for replacement locomotives on the grounds of economy - it was cost-effective to keep adding to existing fleets in the interest of standardisation, and the LDO was busy turning out the required drawings as Grouping approached. Much as he would have liked to replace the NCC fleet with new more modern types, the small numbers involved of these non-standard 5 ft 3 in. gauge examples precluded a major design exercise. He did, however, manage to introduce more standard MR features and fittings in addition to the standard boiler used on the 4-4-0s of 1914. In later years Fowler expertise was to appear on the NCC in the form of a 2-6-0 adaptation of the 2-6-4T, and that is dealt with in Chapter Eleven.

One other matter which influenced the way in which the NCC need was met revolved around the political situation in Ireland at that time, in that it was not clear until 1921 that partition, with Ulster remaining as part of the UK, was to happen. If Ulster had been forced to become part of the Irish Free State the NCC would probably have passed out of the hands of the MR.

To return to the more personal side of things, in keeping with his cycling interest, Sir Henry encouraged other members of the family to adopt this form of transport as a means of travelling on holiday. Eleven-year-old Eric very much enjoyed his father's company and so, in September 1922, accompanied him to France for a fortnight's holiday. First they and their bicycles travelled by sea and rail to Arles in the South of France from where they set off on an extensive cycling tour of the area. Their itinerary was meticulously planned by Henry in keeping with his natural organisational skills and, although some diversions from the original occurred, the trip was substantially as laid out. The full facts of their journeyings were typed up on their return and a copy of this still exists, being illustrated opposite. Sir Henry must indeed have been in good fettle to manage many cycling trips, some of 50 km, on this holiday.

Quite often, Eric would accompany his father to the Derby works on a Saturday, being allowed to roam around with him as he marched around making his presence known: 'If they are in on Saturday, so should I be' is a typical quote, according to Eric. So long as there was a six-day week for the workforce (although Saturday working was now mornings only) he felt it was his duty to do likewise.

```
Sunday   August 27th.  Derby    --    --    Dep. 7.  2 pm.

                        St Pancras          arr. 9. 47  ,
                        ─────────────────────────────────
Monday     ,,  28th.    Victoria         dep. 9. 15 am. 2 Ordinary seats
                                                            reserved,
                        Boulogne         arr.12. 45 pm.
                           ,,            dep. 1. 27  , ) 2 Tickets for first
                                                      )            lunch.
                        Paris            arr. 4. 35  , )
                           ,,   (P.L.M.) dep. 8. 25  , -- " Couchettes
                                                            reserved.
Tuesday    ,,  29th.    Arles            arr. 8. 24 am )
                                                       ) Hotel du Forum.
                           ,,            dep. 6.  3 pm )
                        St Gilles        arr. 6. 35  ,
                           ,,            dep. 8.  6  ,
                        Arles            arr. 8. 32  ,         ,,
Wednesday  ,,  30th.       ,,            dep. 8. 15 am

                        Stes.Maries      arr.

         Cycled from Stes.Maries to Aimargues.

                        Aimargues        dep. 7. 21 pm
                        Arles            arr. 8. 32  ,         ,,
Thursday August 31st.  Cycled from Arles to Avignon.

Friday   Sept.  1st.    Avignon.         --       -- Hotel Louvre.

Saturday   ,,   2nd.   Cycled from Avignon to Nimes, via Pont de Gard.

Sunday     ,,   3rd.    Nimes.           ,-       -- Hotel Luxemburg.
Monday     ,,   4th.       ,,  (P.L.M.)  dep. 8. 32 am.

                        Cette            arr.10.  4  ,
                           ,,  (Midi).   dep.10. 20  ,
                        Narbonne         arr.11, 35  ,

         Cycled from Narbonne to Lezignan.

                        Lezignan         dep. 4. 42 pm.
                        Carcassonne      arr. 5.  2  ,
Tuesday    ,,   5th.    Carcassonne.     --       -- Hotel Bernard.

Wednesday  ,,   6th.       ,,            dep.10. 50 am.

                        Bordeaux         arr. 5, 47 pm. Hotel Terminus.
Thursday   ,,   7th.       ,,            dep.10  15  , 2 Berthed compart'nt
                                                        (wagon-lits)
                                                          reserved.
Friday     ,,   8th     Paris (Q.d'Orsay) arr. 8. 11 am.


Friday  Sept. 8th.      Paris  (Nord)    dep. 3. 30 pm.) 2 Seats
                                                       )  reserved.
                        Calais           arr. 8. 30  , )
                                 (Hotel Maritime).
Saturday   ,,   9th.       ,,            dep. 6. 15 am.

                        Dover            arr. 7. 45  ,
                           ,,            dep. 8. 25  , ) 2 Seats reserved
                        London           arr. 10.17  , )  in Pullman Car.


                        London (St Pancras) dep. 12, 25 pm.
                        DERBY               arr.  2. 54  ,
```

The itinerary for Sir Henry and Eric's cycling holiday in the South of France, 1922.

Mrs D. Fowler

```
Arles to Les Baux. ─────────── 17 K.
Les Baux to St Remi. ──── 10.5
St Remi to Avignon. ──── 23.5.
Arles to Tarascon ───── 14.0.
Tarascon to Avignon ─ ─ ─ 25.0.
Arles to Nimes ─ ── ── 27.5.
Arles to St Gilles ─ ─ ─ 18.0.
Arles to Stes Maries ─ ─ 38.5.
    via St Gilles   55.5.
Stes Maries to Aigues Mortes. ─── 30.0.
Avignon to Pont du Gard. ─ alors 20:0.
Pont du Gard to Nimes ── 19.0.
Nimes to Aigues Mortes ──· 39:0.
Aigues Mort to Montpellier. ─ 36.5.
Nimes to Montpelier via Lunel 50.0
Montpelier to Beziers via agde ── 79.0.
Beziers to Carcassonne ─── 75.0
```

Chapter Seven

Grouping

The British Government's plans for nationalising the railway system having been dropped in favour of the Grouping proposed by Sir Eric Geddes, the then Minister of Transport, resulted in the Railways Act of 1921 being passed for implementation in January 1923.

The main railways which were to form the London, Midland and Scottish Railway (LMS) comprised the London and North Western (LNWR), Lancashire & Yorkshire, Midland, North Staffordshire and Furness railways in England plus the Caledonian, Highland and Glasgow & South Western (G&SWR) railways in Scotland as the main constituents. The LNWR and L&YR had, in fact, merged in 1922 which had resulted in George Hughes being appointed CME of the joint concern, displacing H.P.M. Beames at Crewe on the grounds of seniority, Hughes being aged 57 as against Beames 47.

Hughes had a long and distinguished record with the L&YR and, in fact, we have seen that he and Henry Fowler were old colleagues of Horwich days, and so the rapport between them obviously smoothed things over at Grouping when Fowler himself was displaced to the position of Deputy CME, whilst still remaining in charge at Derby.

One might think that the appointment of Hughes would open the door to a large engine policy, for he was actively engaged in studies for a Pacific for passenger work and a 2-8-2 for freight traffic, both four-cylindered. His existing 4-6-0 of 1908 was being rebuilt and much improved from the original and a further batch of 25 were being laid down at the time of Grouping. However, the strong personality of Sir Guy Granet, Deputy Chairman, in the Boardroom of the LMS held such sway that his Midland background, and hence the small engine policy, was promoted fully. In fact, it has been suggested that much of the terms of the amalgamation were laid down by him. Granet also had considerable backing from James Anderson, shortly to be Superintendent of Motive Power, whom we have seen was a strong proponent of the Midland small engine policy. It is perhaps relevant at this point to emphasise the guiding reason for this policy, this being the weight restrictions on the MR caused by civil engineering limits on bridges, etc. These limits, however, were *not* applicable to the other regions of the LMS. Those Directors from the MR on the LMS Board strongly supported Granet and Anderson and their thinking was coloured by the opinion that anything which came from Derby *must* be superior to any product of Horwich, Crewe or St Rollox, the other three main production centres for the LMS. This was a dangerous and retrograde precedent, for Hughes was already a strong proponent of long travel valves and large generous bearings, plus improved tolerances on manufacture. In the latter context micrometers had been introduced on the production line at Horwich. This is not to say that all at Derby were against long travel and improved clearances, as many of the younger elements in the Locomotive Drawing Office were very much in favour, but tended to be over-ruled by their seniors, who were in the main, well steeped in Derby traditions. For example, a maximum of 3¾ inch valve travel was often mentioned as the acceptable figure for standard use. There was a distinct worry about wear on moving surfaces producing high repair costs. Although it should be stated that a locomotive employing long lap, long travel valves, by virtue of its freer exhaust, invariably runs at a shorter cut-off and thus shorter valve travel, when well linked up. The wear that occurs would therefore be no worse than the short travel valves.

Hughes, whose LNWR/L&YR headquarters were at Horwich, had a relatively modern works and offices and a design team well used to the application of new ideas. Derby, for the time being took a back seat, but moves were afoot to organise a change once Hughes was gone in a few years' time. To implement this, Anderson was replaced by S.J. Symes as Works Manager, with Symes' chief draughtsman's position being taken by H. Chambers. Anderson's immediate superior in his Motive Power Superintendentcy was, however, another ex-Midland man, J.H. Follows. So he was in some respect protected from the strong LNWR derived Motive Power Department staff, who obviously would be supportive of *their* ways when it came to the knotty problem of new locomotives.

Henry Fowler, although obviously aware of a situation whereby the new CME might be in a remote and, possibly, difficult position with the Board, consolidated his position as Deputy CME by taking on the responsibility for overseeing the continued preparations for production and development of Midland types needed for expansion and replacement of the older medium powered locomotives. He also instigated some studies at Derby into a three-cylinder compound 4-6-0 based on a stretch of the existing 4-4-0 compound.

The ubiquitous compound. Here is a works picture of the first of the Fowler 6 ft 9 in. version built at Derby in 1924. Some 195 were to be built through to 1932.

JSM Collection

Hughes decided to remain established at Horwich, where he had hoped to create an effective design leadership, but the Board's decisions on the main thrust of locomotive developments certainly had an effect on his aspirations. However, whilst he attempted to put his own plans forward as to the way matters should go, he must have sensed that the battle ahead should be handed over to a younger person for greater continuity of application. The big restocking and standardisation programme that was clearly needed was obviously going to take some considerable time.

The standard design programme began with Hughes deciding on an 0-6-0T for shunting and light duties being a suitable design to commence with. He put the task out to Fowler at Derby, who ordered the LDO to prepare drawings taking the Johnson 0-6-0T of 1899 as a starting point, but specifying a Belpaire boiler, enlarged bunker and extended smokebox. The design was speedily completed and ordered into quantity production; useful and reliable little locomotives, they were eventually to be found all over the LMS and were to become more generally known as the 'Jinty'. No less than 422 were built between 1924 and 1930, none at Derby works, but all were contracted out: to the Vulcan Foundry (120), North British (75), Hunslet (90), Bagnall (32), Beardmore (90) and Horwich (15).

Whilst he continued in office, Hughes added to his project plans by instigating discussions with Beyer, Peacock concerning a possible Garratt development, to be considered as an alternative to the 2-8-2 project. Beyer, Peacock recommended a 2-6-2+2-6-2 layout in these tentative approaches. By the time a Garratt was to be seriously considered, Hughes had retired and the influence of Derby ideas affected matters adversely, as we shall see later.

About a year before Grouping, the Horwich design office had begun scheming a mixed-traffic 2-6-0. Design of this continued and it became the first completely new type to be ordered by the LMS, although production was not to be instigated until after Hughes had retired.

So far as new locomotives were concerned, 1923 was a dead year. Little in the way of production was achieved as the LMS Board and senior officers planned for future developments. Many outdated designs needed replacing, having had heavy use during the war years. In addition, some degree of standardisation was needed to overcome the large number of locomotive types from the constituent railways now under one system.

As far as his outside interests were concerned, Henry Fowler had been elected a Vice-President of the I.Mech.E. the previous year and, in 1923 was elected President of the Engineering Section of the British Association, so the rounds of meetings still took much of his spare time.

The battle for supremacy in the choice of locomotive policy was well and truly on, with Hughes and Fowler both affected by decisions at Board level. James Anderson, in his capacity of Superintendent of Motive Power had, as did Hughes, direct access to the Board and appeared to be somewhat unofficially involved in the design aspects, this stemming from his earlier MR days as chief locomotive draughtsman. This will be covered in more detail later.

One early task that Hughes needed to address was that of Crewe Works' reorganisation. This was the largest manufacturing site on the LMS and required

0-6-0T designed as standard type at Derby, here No. 16442, built in 1926 by North British, rests with a Webb 0-6-0ST.   *R.S. Carpenter Collection*

Hughes 2-6-0, which became a standard type for the LMS. A functional and sturdy engine, rather spoilt by the narrow Fowler tender.   *R.S. Carpenter Collection*

a major updating to eliminate some of the oldest buildings and, more importantly, to make some cost savings as the old working practices still in use were very labour intensive. With labour costs now much higher due to the inflationary effects of the war some attempts at economies were needed. Additionally, many of the machines still in use dated back to the late 19th century.

Having paid a visit to Crewe himself, Hughes asked Henry Fowler to carry out a further inspection in greater detail on his behalf (probably he thought that a second opinion would be benefitial, he had already found the matters mentioned above for himself). Fowler reported to him thus:

> I fully appreciate the object you have in view of shutting down the shops that are so old as those near the station. But I would refer to the crowded state which exists in certain of the shops at the steelworks where the work is to be concentrated. No. 9 erecting shop is so congested that I feel some work cannot possibly be carried out on the best lines . . .

Hughes bided his time in bringing the Crewe reorganisation up to Board level, as he needed to gather more evidence for a cast-iron case to be made. He also wished to get the steel-making plant completely replaced and put that at the top of his priorities, as the steel plant at Horwich was to be closed and the Crewe plant would become the major producer for the LMS. It made sense to renew with modern equipment and facilities to cover the anticipated 80,000 tons per year output.

Fowler had a series of meetings with Beames, who had accepted the rather downwards move from Deputy CME of the LNWR/L&YR to that of Divisional Mechanical Engineer, Crewe, although without any salary reduction, as ordered by the Board. As a result of these meetings Beames was asked to take command of the Crewe reorganisation, reporting to Hughes and Fowler.

Beames had, in the recent past, been despatched to the USA to view production methods there and had seen the 'belt' or 'flow-line' method of production and repair of locomotives in operation, and offering much reduced times for assembly and servicing. This was put forward as being well worth considering for adoption, for as things stood, the time to pass a locomotive through the works for a major overhaul was of the order of 40 days, or 75 locomotives per month. 'Flow-line' techniques offered reductions in times of up to 60 per cent with a corresponding increase in locomotive output to over 110 per month. The cost savings were also apparent in other ways, in that 20 per cent fewer men were needed to accomplish the tasks, plus the fact that engines would be out of revenue-earning traffic for less time.

Once Fowler had studied and approved Beames proposals, the plan was authorised and alterations at Crewe works began. Immediately the reorganisation had been completed the improvements in repair time were evident and the results made known to other railways via the ARLE regular meetings. This was in early 1927, and Henry Fowler, by then the CME, immediately invited other CME's to visit Crewe to see the new system in operation, Maunsell and Gresley being the first two to respond. Both were very impressed by what they saw, Maunsell in particular, who returned to Waterloo and ordered his staff to prepare schemes for 'flow-line' techniques to be applied at the Eastleigh locomotive works and the Lancing carriage works of the Southern.

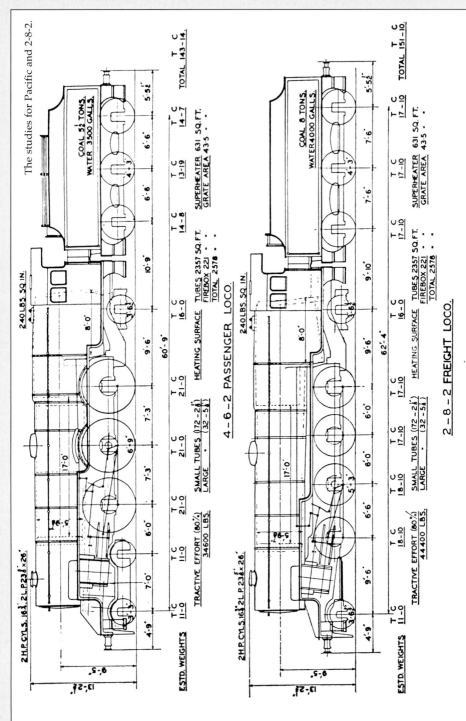

The studies for Pacific and 2-8-2.

4-6-2 PASSENGER LOCO.

240 LBS. SQ IN.

COAL 5½ TONS,
WATER 3500 GALLS.

2 H.P.CYLS. 16¼" 2 L.P.23¼" × 26"

	T C		T C		T C		T C		T C		T C		T C		T C		T C		T C
ESTD. WEIGHTS	11-0		21-0		21-0		21-0		16-0		14-8		13-19		14-7				

4'-9" · 7'-0" · 6'-0" · 7'-3" · 7'-3" · 9'-6" · 10'-9" · 6'-6" · 6'-6" · 5'-5½"

60'-9"

17'-0"   3'-6½"   8'-0"

9'-5"
13'-2½"

TRACTIVE EFFORT (80%) 34600 LBS.

SMALL TUBES (172 - 2⅛")
LARGE ″ (32 - 5⅛")

HEATING SURFACE TUBES 2357 SQ. FT.
FIREBOX 221 ″ ·
TOTAL 2578 ″ ·

SUPERHEATER 631 SQ. FT.
GRATE AREA 43·5 ″ ·

TOTAL T C 143-14.

---

2 - 8 - 2 FREIGHT LOCO.

240 LBS. SQ IN.

COAL 8 TONS,
WATER 4000 GALLS.

2 H.P.CYLS. 16½" 2 L.P.23½" × 26"

	T C		T C		T C		T C		T C		T C		T C		T C		T C		T C
ESTD. WEIGHTS	11-0		18-10		18-10		17-10		16-0		17-10		17-10		17-10				

4'-9" · 9'-6" · 6'-6" · 6'-0" · 6'-0" · 9'-6" · 9'-10" · 7'-6" · 7'-6" · 5'-5½"

62'-4"

17'-0"   5'-3"   3'-6½"   8'-0"

9'-5"
13'-2½"

TRACTIVE EFFORT (80%) 44400 LBS.

SMALL TUBES (172 - 2⅛")
LARGE ″ (32 - 5⅛")

HEATING SURFACE TUBES 2357 SQ. FT.
FIREBOX 221 ″ ·
TOTAL 2578 ″ ·

SUPERHEATER 631 SQ. FT.
GRATE AREA 43·5 ″ ·

TOTAL T C 151-10.

SIR HENRY FOWLER'S DESIGNS FOR LARGE 4 CYL. COMPOUND LOCOS. – 1926.

One important feature of the Beames' studies had been that both Hughes and Fowler asked that these should take account for larger locomotives than were current. Fowler was, we have seen, engaged in a 4-6-0 compound study and Hughes had the Horwich drawing office looking at more Pacific and 2-8-2 layouts. From this one can see the thinking of the two engineers moving towards larger locomotives for the near future. Unfortunately Anderson was on another wave-length for entirely different matters, as we shall see later. However, his influence was not to upset Hughes' and Fowler's arguments for time and cost savings were very attractive to the LMS Board at a time when economy commensurate with expansion was the watchword.

Matters at Derby started to accelerate in 1923 and 1924, in that a batch of new 4-4-2T tanks was needed for the former London, Tilbury & Southend portion of the LMS. This had been taken over in 1912 by the MR and run as a more or less separate arm since then. The new tanks were in the main based on the current design in service, but had some LMS standard parts incorporated and the boiler redesigned and improved, and were soon in service on the frequent commuter runs for which they were needed.

A big engine policy continued to be promoted by Hughes, with yet another new design to emanate from Horwich. The LMS had, at Grouping, inherited a mixed bag of Baltic tanks, eight from the LT&SR arm, five from the Furness Railway and six from the G&SWR. Big, heavy locomotives all of them, they had the advantage of being capable of fast running in either direction, thus eliminating turning at the end of their (predominately passenger) journeys. Hughes, however, clearly had his own ideas as to future developments in the 4-6-4T sphere and started his team on a Baltic development of his 4-6-0, then in series production at Horwich and Crewe.

Ten of this tank design were outshopped in 1924 and entered service. So now the LMS had no fewer than 29 Baltic tanks of four classes! Hardly a recipe for standardisation, though obviously Hughes hoped that large engines could be standardised around his 4-6-0 design.

Fowler's thoughts on this are not on record, but he must have viewed this adding to the large tank fleet with some distaste, particularly as all these varied types were, by Midland standards, rather weighty. The only class which ventured much onto ex-MR metals were the LT&SR eight, which had spent some two years relegated to coal traffic between Wellingborough and Brent before being divided between the LT&SR (five) and St Albans locals to St Pancras (three). Withdrawals commenced in 1929 and all had gone in five years.

Sir Henry's father died on 1st July, 1924, aged 81, and the family travelled to Evesham for the funeral. This town of his birth was always a favourite place to visit and Henry needed little persuasion to go there, although this particular time the memories conjured up would have been sad ones now that his father was no longer around.

September 1924 found Eric Fowler *en route* to Oundle School, following in brother Harry's footsteps. His Common Entrance results plus his brother's previous attendance ensured a place at this premier Public School. He was to distinguish himself both academically and as a sportsman over the next five years.

4-4-2Ts for the LT&SR arm continued to be built. In 1923 a batch of ten were turned out, here No. 2113 of that batch rests on shed at Shoeburyness in 1936. *H.F. Wheeller Collection*

Whitelegg's large 4-6-4T for the LT&SR. Reputedly one of these achieved 94 mph on trials with Whitelegg himself driving. What the resulting ride was like has not been recorded but one suspects it was quite probably hair-raising. *John Scott-Morgan Collection*

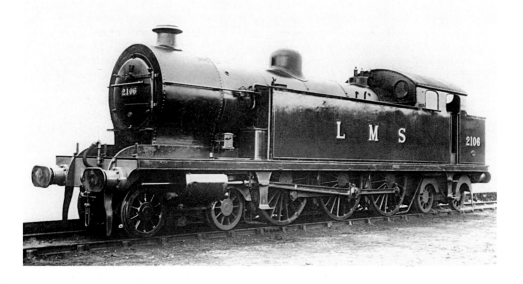

Hughes 4-6-4T variant of his 4-6-0.   *R.S. Carpenter Collection*

These 4-6-4Ts of Hughes were large engines as borne out by this photograph of No. 11113
awaiting departure in 1925.   *R.S. Carpenter Collection*

A typical turn for the 2-6-0 was express work. Here No. 13016 hauls a rake of ex-GCR stock out of Huddersfield *en route* for Sheffield and Marylebone in 1927. This view shows the disparity in tender width to better advantage.   *R.S. Carpenter Collection*

Hughes 4-6-0 No. 10456 was selected for conversion to a 4-cylinder compound in 1925 and served faithfully until withdrawn and scrapped by Stanier some 10 years later. Here seen at Carlisle Upperby in 1930-2.   *R.S. Carpenter Collection*

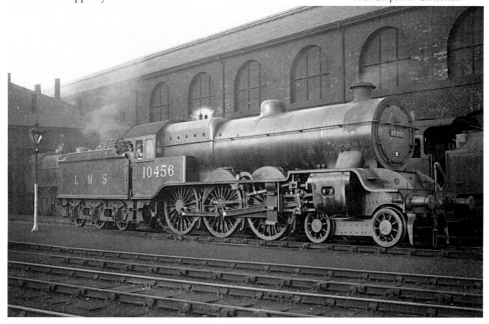

The scheming of the Pacific and 2-8-2 continued at Horwich and had reached the stage of being considered as compounds. This finally awoke the Locomotive Committee to authorise two prototypes of the Pacific in 1925. After some four years of sporadic design effort this was welcome. Hughes accordingly gave orders that, in some effort to integrate the design teams, Derby should be delegated to design the boiler and Crewe the cylinder assembly for these two large prototypes. Anderson must have viewed this with some alarm - it went against his ingrained small engine policy - and resolved that, once matters were right, a move to stop further work would be made. Progress was accordingly slow.

Beames at Crewe, however, was all for the larger engines and saw to it that the cylinders were designed speedily. In fact, he had the working drawings and tools ready in late 1925 and had actually cast some sets of cylinders.

Hughes, by this time, was getting ready to retire. His attempts to get what he thought was needed adopted by the LMS Board were clearly being thwarted, and without any mandate to follow a large engine policy his design leadership was in question. A younger man was needed to counteract the problems in administration and integration of the two main design organisations, Horwich/Crewe and Derby. Therefore, in October 1925, he retired at his own request and moved to Cromer and settled down to indulge himself in his favourite hobby of horticulture, for 20 years, until his death in 1945 just after his 80th birthday. His quiet but firm demeanour was much missed by the team at Horwich, who had just completed the detail design of the mixed-traffic 2-6-0 which was to be adopted as a standard type by the LMS. There was also a diagram on the boards for a 2-6-4T variant for passenger working over the system.

Horwich works continued building sporadically until 1957, when it turned out the last locomotive to emerge from the shops, a BR Standard 2-6-0.

1925 was important in that it was the Centenary of the opening of the Stockton and Darlington Railway, so it was natural for the International Railway Congress to fix its 10th session in London. Fowler had been appointed Joint General Secretary for this event and had much to do in connection with the organisation of the Congress. The proceedings were formally opened by H.R.H. The Duke of York in the hall of the Institution of Civil Engineers with the GWR Chairman, Viscount Churchill, presiding. Several days of meetings then ensued with papers on five main subjects: Ways and Works, Locomotives and Rolling Stock, Working of Railways, General Matters and Light Railways and Colonial Railways. There was a field trip to the GWR works at Swindon and the Session culminated with a banquet for the 1,400 attendees and guests at the Crystal Palace. Following the Congress many delegates took advantage of the opportunity to travel to Darlington for the Centenary Exhibition commemorating the 100 years that had passed since the opening of the Stockton & Darlington Railway. In the cavalcade of trains assembled from all the main railways in the UK, the LMS offering consisted of a Hughes 4-6-0 at the head of the latest LMS restaurant car set built recently at Derby for the West Coast services. Interestingly, the LNER offering for the cavalcade of passenger trains was made up of Raven Pacific *City of Newcastle* hauling the latest 'Flying Scotsman' stock, even though the usual locomotive for this premier express was the Gresley Pacific. The Raven engine was, after all, a Darlington design.

Ex-LNWR 'Prince of Wales' class 4-6-0 No. 5600 *Prince of Wales* at Nottingham Carriage Sidings.
Rail Archive Stephenson

Ex-LNWR 'Claughton' 4-6-0 No. 6023 *Sir Charles Cust* seen at Crewe in July 1939. This locomotive was rebuilt with Caprotti valvegear in August 1926 and received a large boiler in December 1928.   *Rail Archive Stephenson*

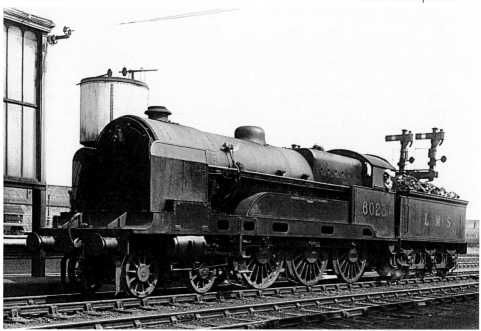

Shortly after this event, Sir Henry Fowler was appointed a member of the permanent commission of the International Railway Congress Association (IRCA) and he added this post to his burgeoning list of organisations to which he had a responsibility.

The LMS Board still had a large number of ex-MR Directors and Sir Guy Granet as Chairman who, with Hughes gone, seized the opportunity to get Derby back as the design centre. Henry Fowler was thus appointed as CME of the LMS, and with this design leadership transferred to Derby, with retrograde effects due to the still prevalent small engine policy, until events permitted him to reverse this outdated situation.

The LMS was, however, a much larger concern than the old MR with many long distance runs, both passenger and freight, required. Despite this fact, with design leadership back at Derby, the plan to promote MR types as standard for the whole system continued.

In this context, Hughes had made known his wish to retire some months previous to his 60th birthday and it is thought that Anderson, learning of this, had prevailed on the Board to allow some comparitive trials in May 1925 between MR, LNWR and L&YR locomotives. The comparison was between two class '4' engines, a LNWR 'Prince of Wales' and MR compound and two class '5' 4-6-0s, these being a L&YR Hughes 4-6-0 as recently rebuilt and a LNWR 'Claughton'. The best overall coal consumption in lb./dhp. hour was obtained from the Compound, but the 'Claughton' produced the lowest figure in terms of lb. per train mile. The former figure was used as a basis to continue the 4-4-0 fleet expansion despite the obvious restriction on train weights for this type. Hughes had no say in the interpretation of this data, however, as he was out of the way when it was published. Meantime, in the 18 months up to his retirement, some 86 more compounds had been built at Derby (70) and Horwich (16). Anderson's pressure on the Locomotive Committee had prevailed thus far.

On the matter of affairs external to the LMS scene, some time after having established himself at Spondon Hall, Sir Henry's attention was drawn to the high retaining wall either side of the main driveway entrance. This was beginning to bulge out towards the road under the pressure of the accumulated soil it had been erected to hold back. He had some retaining works installed, these resulting in two large retaining irons, one each side of the entrance. The one on the left was made in the shape of the letter 'H', that on the right the letter 'F'. Sadly, when the site of Spondon Hall was redeveloped years later, these rather unique fixtures were scrapped, Quite probably, they had been made in the forge at Derby works.

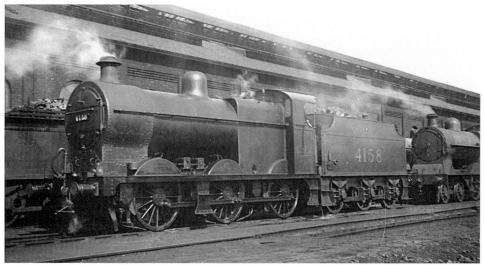

'4F' class 0-6-0 No. 4158, built at Crewe in 1925, rests at Derby *c.* 1930. *R.S. Carpenter Collection*

Yet another '4F' for the LMS. Here one of the 1926 batch is under construction on 6th June of that year.   *National Railway Museum*

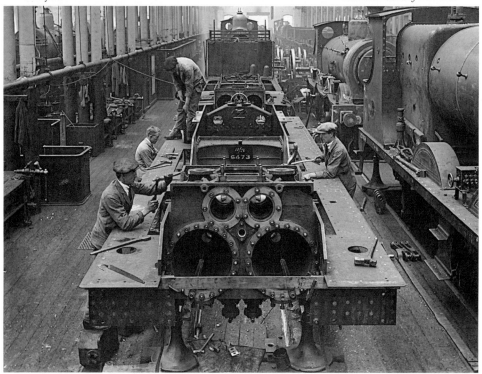

Chapter Eight

Back to the CME's Chair

The appointment of Henry Fowler as CME was seen as an attempt by the Board, who still had a large vocal ex-MR membership, to place someone in that job who would not upset the applecart and who would be pliable enough to enable policy matters to be settled without much argument. After all, Sir Henry's popularity and affability was, by now, a feature of his life. Additionally, as Hughes' deputy, he was the logical follow-on candidate for a smooth transfer of authority. His outside interests still flourished, indeed he was once reported to have stated that his only enemy was time. Life was full for him as well as Emma, who had recently been appointed as a Magistrate in Derby.

Fowler's initial responsibilities found him in charge of all design and manufacture at Crewe, Derby, Horwich and St Rollox which also involved liaison with Works Managers on matters associated with the control of steel works, rolling mills and foundries. The relatively smooth way in which all this functioned during his time as CME is a tribute to his organisational skills and leadership. As one of his main interests was in the materials area, his metallurgical interests seeing to that, whilst he was CME he insisted that meticulous records were kept of each batch of material entering the respective works, and on which locomotive these materials were used. It was a party piece of his to demonstrate this to visitors by reference to a locomotive nearby and requesting the materials records of, say, the steel used in the tyres, in what became known as 'the permissible limit' - usually five minutes!

One of the first priorities, so far as the design matters were concerned, was to get the current project studies transferred to Derby for investigation as to their potential. So, down from Horwich appeared five schemes, in different stages of completion. These were firstly the compound Pacific which had got to the stage of detail design and some manufacture; secondly the freight compound 2-8-2 study, thirdly the 2-6-0 already at an advanced stage in the shops, fourthly a set of diagrams for a 2-6-4T variant of the 2-6-0 and, finally some brief schemes for a Garratt type to be developed in conjunction with Beyer, Peacock. When one realises that only the Pacific and the 2-8-2 were to fall by the wayside, one begins to understand that had Hughes been allowed to progress in his fashion, matters on the LMS might have been totally different in the context of locomotive developments. More particularly so if he had based himself at Crewe where he would have had strong backing from Beames.

However, with compound 4-4-0s in large-scale production, together with continued series production of '4F' 0-6-0s, the small engine policy looked set to take over. Integration of the locomotive policy on the LMS seemed as remote as ever. The rivalries between the MR and LNWR/L&YR teams defied all attempts to produce an acceptable and rational policy.

Henry Fowler, on being given the CME position, could have made a move to integrate the teams at one location, he had the mandate to do this, but preferred not to rock the boat by proposing such a radical step. Instead he ordered that the ex-North Staffordshire Railway drawing office at Stoke be closed, with the staff divided between Crewe and Derby. The chief draughtsman from Stoke, A.E. Owen, was moved to Derby to become Chamber's deputy. Also a few staff were moved from St Rollox and Horwich to Derby. The remaining senior positions at Derby continued to be held by ex-MR persons. With the influx of these extra draughtsmen, the LDO was expanded into the area on the second floor 'under the Clock' previously occupied by the electrical staff. Chambers continued as chief draughtsman, a conscientious person according to contemporary accounts, touring the LDO every week, but showing little design leadership, preferring to leave those matters in the hands of the leading draughtsmen. The two key such persons were Henderson and Campbell, both Scots and not the sort to take on new technology easily, preferring their old well-tried techniques. Henderson in the main checked the drawings issued for dimensional accuracy and acted as a go-between for Chambers and the staff. Campbell, on the other hand, did show interest in individuals' work, but politely urged them to keep to the old and safe, which thankfully was not always done, as we shall see concerning the valve gear episode on the 2-6-4T exercise.

Fowler's prolific outside interests also ensured that his time devoted to important matters was limited to normal working hours. He continued to dash everywhere, even being said to dictate memoranda, whilst walking at his usual speedy pace, to a clearly frustrated clerk.

The compound designs for the Pacific and 2-8-2 have, it appears, been attributed to Fowler, but one only has to look at the drawings to see that here are two purely Hughes' locomotives in terms of styling. Fowler 'adopted' them as a means of providing evidence that the CME's office could provide answers to a problem raised in connection with three-cylinder compounds. For by this time the Derby LDO had produced some diagrams for a 4-6-0 'stretch' of the 4-4-0 compound for, specifically, West Coast main line duties. This however died when evidence of inefficiency in the three-cylinder compound layout was presented by E.L. Diamond, one of Sir Henry's pupils, in a paper analysing some indicator trials on the three-cylinder compounds Nos. 1060 and 1065. The paper, given to the Graduates and Students Section of the I.Mech.E., was entitled 'An Investigation into the Cylinder Losses in a Compound Locomotive' and showed the extent of throttling losses as being half the power available to haul the train.

Fowler was in the audience and obtained a copy of the paper, took it back to Derby and put aside the 4-6-0 compound and switched more effort to the four-cylinder compound Pacific and 2-8-2, which offered lower cylinder losses and therefore greater tractive efficiency.

We have seen that the Pacific had actually been authorised and manufacture started. However, it appears that it was Anderson who prevailed with the Board to have it cancelled - on the grounds that it was too long to fit on many of the turntables on the Midland section - stating that the replacement cost of these would be a prohibitively expensive exercise. Fowler thus received orders to cease work on the Pacific. He was, to say the least, rather put out by this interferance in his plans, but true to form, complied with the directive, not wishing to create any high-level arguments. Hughes had ordered the conversion of one of his redesigned 4-6-0's to a four-cylinder compound just before he retired, and this was to enter service in 1926, with No. 10456 of the final 1924 batch being selected as the guinea pig. This had entered traffic and was showing considerable economies in water and coal consumption. The results of trials with this locomotive obviously gave a strong case to Fowler for the Pacific proposal. However, Derby thinking reigned supreme and, although this conversion served reliably no further conversions were ordered and, in 1936, the sole example was withdrawn by Stanier.

As 1926 progressed, the building of new locomotives gathered pace, with Derby, Horwich, St Rollox and Crewe at full capacity. Considerable use of outside contractors was needed to satisfy the demand. This practice was, over the following three years to increase, with some nine different companies being involved.

There was an important change at the top of the LMS management in 1926 when Sir Josiah Stamp was brought in by the Chairman, Sir Guy Granet, to apply his expertise to sorting out the management structure. Stamp was a Director of ICI and a brilliant economist. Originally he had been offered the post of General Manager, but his previous experience with big business in the USA made him suggest that the LMS adopt the American type of business organisation. This was the precept that company policy was decided by a President aided by a small number of Vice-Presidents responsible for various departments, with the management details left to the respective heads of departments.

On his appointment, effective from January 1926, Stamp immediately started taking stock of practice on the LMS. One of his first questions was to ask why, when the heavy express trains of other railways were almost always hauled by a single locomotive, those out of Euston and St Pancras were so frequently double-headed. The answers he got failed to impress him and he immediately pressured Fowler to do something about this.

Sir Henry must have felt very frustrated by this request, as it had only been a short time ago that the compound Pacific had been cancelled and such components as had been made scrapped. However, he was to be overtaken by events for it was around this time that the legendary Pacific/'Castle' exchange between the LNER and GWR had taken place, with the result that the GWR locomotive came out far superior to the LNER Pacific. Sir Guy Granet was a close friend of Sir Felix Pole, General Manager of the GWR, and it is generally thought that Granet, at some time, brought up the subject of LMS motive power needs. The net result was that Fowler was informed that a 'Castle' class 4-6-0 was to be lent to the LMS and that a series of tests, using the dynamometer car, would be made between Euston and Carlisle. Fowler would have no jurisdiction over the testing, as this would be under Anderson as Superintendent of Motive Power.

The tests were made in two sections, firstly from Euston to Crewe and secondly from Crewe to Carlisle. In fact the dynamometer car, from Horwich, was only used on the second section. On the first, southern, set of trials, with train loads of 470-500 tons, the Castle showed considerable improvements in timings, and on the northern section coped well with loads up to 430 tons unassisted over Shap Fell. Coal consumption was better than that of the compounds.

The tests were completed on 20th November, 1926, and shortly afterwards Fowler was ordered to provide 50 'Improved Castles' for the following summer's traffic which was to include through workings from Euston to Glasgow and Edinburgh.

The story of how this was actually achieved is a classic example of Fowler at his best - organising and planning with the Derby LDO and the outside contractors involved, the North British Locomotive Company.

The LMS firstly approached Swindon for a set of 'Castle' drawings, the idea being to use these, suitably modified to incorporate Derby parts and ideas, to 'short-cut' the design task, so little time being available. Fowler was, it is thought, not involved in this request and it says something of his character that he did not blow his top at this obvious affront to his position. In fact, it put him in a good position to make a similar move elsewhere after Swindon refused to condone any such supply of technical information. He felt that as those above him had had the nerve to approach another railway for help, he could now do the same without censure. He accordingly paid a visit to his old Horwich colleague, Richard Maunsell, now CME of the Southern Railway, who was more than happy to arrange for a set of 'Lord Nelson' drawings to be supplied to Derby.

Maunsell's 'Nelson' prototype was in service, proving a good performer and exhibiting excellent mechanical reliability and with an order for an initial batch of 10 placed. Fowler ordered that Herbert Chambers, the Derby chief draughtsman, was to commence liaison with Maunsell's team at Waterloo and cast around for a manufacturer willing to take on a lot of detail design and manufacture in a very short time. Derby and the other LMS plants were loaded to capacity and could, under no circumstances, plan for delivery within six months of an order being placed. For that was the time available to meet the traffic department's requirement.

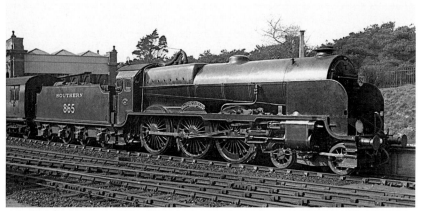

Southern Railway 'Lord Nelson' class 4-6-0 No. 865 *Sir John Hawkins* with a London-bound train at Bournemouth in 1937.   *T.G. Hepburn/Rail Archive Stephenson*

The North British tender of £7,725 per locomotive was accepted and the majority of the design task transferred to them, Chambers making frequent visits to Glasgow to monitor matters. Delivery was optimistically set for the 1927 summer timetable.

Christmas 1926 must have been a short time of welcome relief for the Fowlers as the NBL letter of intent was signed in late December, followed by detailed negotiations leading up to the official order filling the early days of the New Year. The contract became firm in February 1927 and the pace of work in the NBL drawing office and Hyde Park and Queen's Park works picked up as drawings were completed, checked, signed and issued for detail manufacture.

The magnitude of the task facing the drawing office staff of the NBL was immense. Maunsell's design was four-cylindered with a 220 psi boiler. The LMS specification was for three cylinders and a 250 psi boiler. And so it was not surprising that the first production example did not appear until July 1927, a couple of weeks late. All 50 were delivered by November of that year.

Right from the start, the new 4-6-0s, to become known as the 'Royal Scot' class, were a great success in service and on September 26th the new prestige non-stop Euston to Carlisle express, the 'Royal Scot' was inaugurated. The new locomotive coped well with the 15-coach train weighing 420 tons on this long run. Part of the success was due to the incorporation of long travel, long lap valve gear taken from schemes prepared for the 2-6-4T then under development at Derby. Maunsell's design had also exhibited this feature. Also, some of the changes normally required by Derby, such as the inadequate '4F' bearings, were not forced upon the NBL designers, there simply was not time. And the beloved 8 ft + 8 ft 6 in. coupled wheel spacing escaped inclusion, notably resulting in a much more equal distribution of axle loading than that found on other LMS six-coupled types with that 'standard' spacing.

The general likeness to the Maunsell design was there for all to see and Fowler was pleased by the initial performance certainly coming up to expectations. His move to approach Maunsell had definitely produced a winner. The small engine policy was, at last, on the wane.

Another matter of pleasure to Henry Fowler was the performance of the NBL Co. in handling this development. His personal prestige would certainly have benefitted and his moves towards six-coupled express types vindicated. Doubtless Anderson, too, made sure of his own part in the exercise being duly noted to advantage. Small engines were now to be displaced from their central rôle for major express work, and the stage was set for even greater achievements in the 1930s under Stanier.

1927 was a busy year for Fowler. As well as dealing with the four LMS plants, Derby, Crewe, Horwich and St Rollox, he was also involved in contracts placed with no less than seven outside contractors building locomotives ordered. No fewer than 373 locomotives of seven different classes were delivered that year from the 11 sources, representing a peak in the production rate for Fowler's reign.

The workload for this would have been huge, but no better man was to be found capable of dealing with it than Henry Fowler. His aptitude for dealing

'Royal Scot' class No. 6128, as yet un-named at Crewe in 1927. A view from this angle accentuates the large smokebox. Note the crosshead vacuum pump.   *R.S. Carpenter Collection*

No. 6147 *Courier* on a down express in 1933, passing Tring.   *R.S. Carpenter Collection*

swiftly with matters was well exercised and his overall wide-ranging engineering skills played an important part in vetting decisions and suggestions placed before him. Even more, his organisational skills ensured that all the extensive paperwork with outside contractors was carried out efficiently to ensure that deliveries were on time and within cost.

With the country still recovering from the effects of the Great War and the ensuing economic difficulties, the engineering industry needed all the orders it could get to build itself up after the exhausting events of those years. Doubtless the many private locomotive builders were grateful for all the LMS orders as the railway consolidated and standardised its stock.

One important requirement to emanate from the Operating Department, which was outstanding as 1927 approached, was for a powerful and fast passenger tank to be employed on short-range commuter and local traffic throughout the LMS. Fowler, early in the year, had turned to the Hughes' schemes for a 2-6-4T which was originally based on the 2-6-0 by now in production at Horwich and Crewe. The resulting design retained much of the Horwich influence, namely long travel, long lap, valve gear and large generous bearing surfaces, although the final design of valve motion was based on that of Maunsell's 2-6-4T. The draughtsman responsible for this aspect of the design having based his diagrams on the settings of that locomotive as published in the *Railway Gazette*. It was immediately ordered into production once the diagrams had been approved, going into service in 1927. A very successful locomotive, it proved to be capable of speeds up to 80 mph when employed on outer-London suburban trains. The Maunsell 'River' class 2-6-4 tanks were also proving speedy and reliable on some of the Southern's boat expresses and continued use of this type seemed set for some time, when disaster struck in the form of the Sevenoaks crash in which 13 passengers were killed. The Southern tanks were immediately withdrawn from service and, eventually, rebuilt as tender types. Fowler asked Sir John Pringle, the Inspecting Officer of the Ministry of Transport, about the suitability of tank engines of this wheel arrangement. The advice that came back was that the layout would be perfectly all right provided it was not used on fast workings! Fowler ascertained that no reports of unsteady riding of his design existed, and bearing in mind that this problem was most certainly the responsibility of Anderson, made no further moves. The LMS 2-6-4 tanks continued in service, being added to by Stanier, until withdrawal under BR between 1959 and 1966.

As the 1920s progressed, however, several peripheral matters raised their heads in the form of strikes and the economic downturn of the early 1930s as the railways struggled to economise in the inflationary pressures of impending recession. The General Strike of the year before had resulted in a reappearance of oil firing conversions at Derby, with Maunsell on the Southern sending Holcroft to see Fowler and obtain details of the Derby systems derived by him from his research of some years ago. Several examples of Southern locomotives had been converted at Eastleigh following this visit.

The earlier Hughes' studies into the employment of Garratt type locomotives for heavy freight services had, we have seen, resulted in a proposal for a 2-6-2+2-6-2 version being proposed by Beyer, Peacock. However, concurrent to these

Southern Railway 2-cylinder 'River' class 2-6-4T No. A793 *River Ouse* at Brighton.
W.J. Reynolds/Rail Archive Stephenson

The first 2-6-4T, No. 2300, exits the paint shop at Derby, ready for service.
R.S. Carpenter Collection

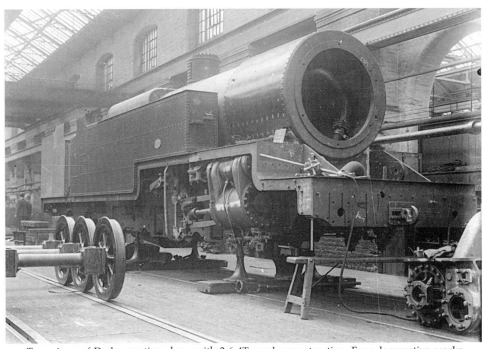

Two views of Derby erecting shop, with 2-6-4Ts under construction. For a locomotive works everything is very tidy indeed! The photographs are dated 1927 and 1933 respectively.

R.S. Carpenter Collection

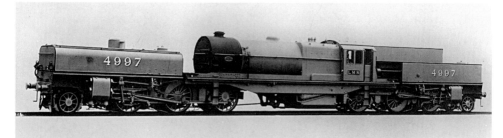

A works photograph of the first 2-6-0+0-6-2 Garratt, built 1927.   *John Scott-Morgan Collection*

Garratt No. 4998 receives some attention to the ashpan at Toton.   *R.S. Carpenter Collection*

The second, 1930, batch of Garratts had rotating self-trimming bunkers. Here No. 4981 passes Elstree with a down coal empties for the Midlands.   *R.S. Carpenter Collection*

discussions by Hughes, it is said that Anderson at Derby had entered into entirely separate discussions with Beyer, Peacock into his own requirements for such a type. His mandate as Superintendent of Motive Power was used as the pretext to visit the company to explain his own ideas on the way things should go. If Hughes had known of this, and it seems inconceivable that he did not, he would have been close to retirement and may have assumed that any design to come from the talks would naturally follow the recommendations of the company holding the Patents. He clearly did not realise the determination of Anderson to continue to promote Derby products and ideas wherever possible. He (Anderson) had *never* been heard to find favour with any product that emanated from anywhere except Derby. Such partisanship was dangerous to the locomotive policy.

So, the LDO at Derby was asked to assemble a package of drawings for Beyer, Peacock, comprising the pony truck and motion of the S&D 2-8-0, and axles and axleboxes of the '4F' 0-6-0, with a 2-6-0+0-6-2 wheel arrangement being specified, even the traditional Derby coupled wheel spacing of 8 ft + 8 ft 6 in. being requested! This was about the middle of 1926, just before the instigation of the 'Royal Scot' episode. By the end of the year the designs had been completed at Beyer, Peacock's, approved, and three examples ordered. Delivery was in July 1927 and Anderson proceeded to inspect the first one, and immediately began to find fault with it. The bunker slope was not steep enough according to his findings and a false wooden floor had to be designed and installed to steepen it. Sundry minor items needed changing, such as sand boxes and standard fittings before he would accept them for traffic. It seems strange that his interference earlier had not been detailed enough to specify such matters, but it had been sufficient to have several negative features to be forced upon the builders, namely the Derby class '4F' axleboxes and short travel valves. The Garratts were always to have problems of hot boxes and were heavy on coal consumption as a result of these relative negative features. The three initial locomotives were put into service on the coal trains and did certainly eliminate the old practice of double-heading. Fowler probably tolerated this clear overruling of his authority because of the extremely heavy workload at that time, coupled to his natural desire to keep a harmonious relationship in the upper echelons of the CME and Motive Power Departments. He probably felt that the expertise of Beyer, Peacock would produce an acceptable design; after all, they were the acknowledged World leaders in such locomotives.

One result of the emergence of the Garratt was that the compound 2-8-2, still on the drawing board, no longer seemed necessary and was quietly scrapped as a potential freight type.

As 1927 progressed, Fowler learned of the University of Birmingham's honour to him, in conferring an LLD degree upon the old student of the Mason Science College, which had formed the core of that university's science facility.

LMS '2P' class 4-4-0 No. 602 at Nottingham carriage sidings.   *Rail Archive Stephenson*

The little 0-6-0T for docks shunting work. Ten were built to designs done at Horwich. No. 11271 pictured at Bow locomotive depot (ex-NLR) in the early 1930s.   *John Scott-Morgan Collection*

Chapter Nine

The Final Years as CME

The year 1927 was also busy for Sir Henry in connection with his professional interests, for he had been elected as President of the Institution of Mechanical Engineers, a prestigious appointment granted due to his long service on the Council and current position on the LMS. His taking office involved the obligatory Presidential address. Sir Henry fell back to his old favourite hobby and prepared a lengthy paper on metallurgy and its advances over the previous century. Developments in the locomotive scene continued, with mixed results throughout the final years of Henry Fowler's CME tenure. There was a pressing need for some medium powered passenger engines to replace many of the obsolescent variants still valiantly serving the LMS. In the interests of economy, the old Midland class '2P' 4-4-0 design was updated, with higher boiler pressure and redesigned cylinders and steam passages to try and improve an indifferent performer. Although the front end was redesigned, no changes were made to either the valve position or travel. As regards position, the valves were left in their original position, *under* the cylinders, never a good location for steam pipes no matter how efficient they were. Short valve travel was also retained, and the first batch were very much the same as the earlier '2Ps', sluggish. Matters were so bad in that respect that subsequent batches were fitted with double exhaust ports to try and remedy the back pressure associated with short travel valves. Nevertheless, despite these shortcomings, some 138 of this version were built and were to be found all over the LMS on light passenger work. If only some notice had been taken of Maunsell's approach to the rebuilding of Wainwright's 'D' and 'E' class 4-4-0s. These had been well publicised for nearly eight years, and the lack of interest at Derby amplified the strict partisan feelings still present in certain areas.

The LDO at Derby, although increased in size, still had to place design work outside, and so when a requirement came for a small tank type to be used in dockyards and confined spaces, the job was delegated to the Horwich design office, then functioning under T.F. Coleman. He designed a functional and easy to maintain 0-6-0T locomotive, which negotiated the tight curves commonplace in such locations. Outside cylinders and Walschaerts valve gear were fitted and the 10 examples were built at Derby in 1928-9, being dispatched to the docks at Birkenhead, Fleetwood and Greenock, where they spent much of their lives. Coleman had originally been chief draughtsman at the Stoke plant of the NSR, and was eventually to come to Derby and replace Chambers when that rather steeped in MR philosophy person was diplomatically elevated to be a personal assistant to Stanier, but that is another story.

The summer of 1927 brought improvements to the 1908 pavilion at the Spondon Cricket Club grounds. At last the facilities were improved with new tea and refreshment rooms being opened. Sir Henry had long advocated this improvement, for his presence on the pitch often drew extra crowds to see him in action and their pangs of hunger would need satisfying. Indeed, there were

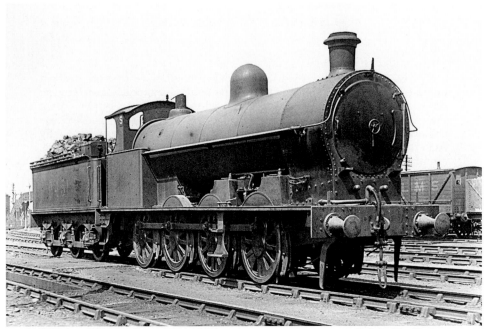

LNWR class 'G2' 0-8-0 'Super D' No. 9451.   *Rail Archive Stephenson*

Fowler 0-8-0, or 'Austin Seven' as it was dubbed. Class '7F' No. 9500 photographed nearly new at Manchester in 1929.   *R.S. Carpenter Collection*

occasions when the Derby County Cricket Club were known to ask the Spondon C.C. to avoid some of their matches clashing with their own if possible, such was the attraction of the amateur side to the local cricket followers.

By late 1927, it seemed at last that the Board of the LMS had decided that the small engine policy, for express and main line freight at least, was dead. They ordered that consideration be given to a standard heavy freight locomotive of the eight-coupled arrangement. The specification for tractive power was set at that equivalent to the class 'G2' of the former LNWR.

The 2-8-0 developed for the S&D was promoted by Derby, it being a basically sound design, and had plenty of potential for development. The LNWR 'G2', designed by Bowen Cooke, as it stood, looked very crude alongside the 2-8-0, but it had been hauling heavy mineral trains reliably for many years.

With two designs to choose from some comparitive assessment was called for, involving road trials and a study of maintenance costs. One of the main uses for the proposed design was the haulage of the Toton-Brent coal trains, and so it was on this run that the trials were made. Almost unbelievably, to Derby people at least, the 'G2' proved best after the first set of runs. The 2-8-0 was taken into Derby works and given a brief overhaul before being returned to the trials. Again the 'G2' came out best, and was selected as the type to be used for the development of the new locomotive.

Fowler agreed to the 'G2' being used as a starting point for the new design, even though the 2-8-0 had been developed under himself, and ordered Chambers to get the LDO to prepare diagrams using the LNWR boiler and a redesigned chassis using inside cylinders, MR style wheels, axles, spring gear, etc.

On major change to the motion was to dispense with Joy's valve gear of the LNWR type and substitute, as it turned out, Walschaerts. The draughtsman chosen for the motion diagrams was young E.A. Langridge, who had been responsible for the setting out of the 2-6-4T long travel gear. Langridge was fully aware of the benefits of long travel, long lap, valves and, on the logical argument that all the NCC locomotives (inside-cylindered) built at Derby had employed inside Walschaerts gear, it was not too difficult to get Chambers to accept its employment.

The resulting 0-8-0 was styled in a typical Fowler way. It weighed no more than the 'G2' and in all 175 were to be produced, all at Crewe. Upon the first examples entering service in 1929, some comparitive trials with the 'G2' were carried out. A 30 per cent saving in coal per drawbar horsepower hour over the 'G2' was measured. However, the employment of the '4F' bearings caused many problems with hot boxes and this spoilt what otherwise was a sound design. Derby *still* relied on an old standard part designed in the days of lighter trains and consequently easier working. The rough and tumble of heavy handling therefore took its toll. The railways, at this time, were always looking for ways to keep costs down and the employment of the '4F' bearings was the result of economic pressure from managers to show maximum economies. But this was a false economy in engineering terms as witness the frequent low mileages run between repairs for these otherwise adequate 0-8-0s. In fact, these new engines were to be outlived by their progenitors, the ex-LNWR 'G2s', which had much more substantial bearings.

By 1928, trials with the three Garretts had proved their suitability for the heavy coal trains and an order was placed with Beyer-Garrett for a further 30. These had sundry minor modifications emanating from the experience with the three examples in service, but unfortunately not in the bearing or valve gear areas.

Henry Fowler, despite all the work going on with locomotive design and production, still kept his outside interests at full stretch. He still played cricket for Spondon, and continued his interest in hockey by writing a regular column, under the pen-name of 'Bully Off', for the *Derby Telegraph*. On matters outside railways and sport, he was deeply involved in Church affairs locally, being a Ruridecanal Conference member, Diocesan Conference member, and on the Diocesan Board of Finance, plus being a delegate to the Church Assembly. On top of all this he still found time to be involved in bell-ringing at his local parish church, St Werburgh's, Spondon.

Taking a leaf out of John Aspinall's book, Sir Henry organised regular tea parties at Spondon Hall, usually on a Sunday afternoon, to which premium apprentices and pupils would be invited, and sized up. His early background on the L&YR under Aspinall encouraged this form of socialising, in order to assess the potential of those aspiring to become engineers or administrators on the railway. These gatherings continued until his retirement.

The honours still came his way, in 1929 from Manchester University, which conferred the Honorary Degree of Doctor of Science on him in June of that year. Sir Henry was presented by Professor S.Alexander, who spoke eloquently about his achievements:

> He has been the parent of many standard types of locomotives, a progeny of beautiful or prodigious monsters, of which the last and most prodigious is the 'Royal Scot'. Innumerable medals or prizes have acknowledged the value of his increasing contributions to engineering science, and with all the engrossing duties of his great domestic office he has contrived to keep abreast of scientific and practical developments abroad and in America, and to adapt them to our advantage.
>
> Above all he is distinguished by his constant effort through personal intercourse to excite a spirit akin to his own of love of their profession among younger engineers, for whom he is a never-failing fountain of enthusiasm and experience distributed through conduits of inexhaustible speech.

The Professor concluded by referring to Sir Henry's life-long association with the more simple mode of transport:

> Least of all would I forget that his concern with greater mechanisms has not blunted his passion for riding the humble, familiar, bicycle.

His Bible Class and its sporting connections still flourished in Spondon, and he still taught as often as possible. On the 10th anniversary of their first post-war reunion, on 30th December, 1929, Henry and Lady Emma held a gathering of old and present members of the class at the Mission Hall in Spondon. Some 60 turned up for this celebration, being entertained by the Fowlers. The guest of honour was Mrs J. Meakin, whose husband was the founder of the class. Some members of the local clergy also joined this group which through the years had caused many young men to become stalwart members of the local church.

There is a story in connection with Sir Henry's social awareness concerning a wedding which took place at St Werburgh's Church on a particularly wet Saturday. The bride, despite running as speedily as she could in her long dress, got rather wet before entering the church. As she waited in the porch for her bridesmaids to adjust her by now slightly bedraggled dress, Sir Henry passed by. The following week, the largest umbrella that could be bought in Derby was delivered to the church, to be used in any future wedding suffering similar weather. The Verger was given strict instructions to be on hand with this umbrella at all times. Despite arriving anonymously, all knew the donor of this thoughtful gift was Sir Henry. It remained in use until it disintegrated through age.

His other outside interests abounded, with practically every important Derby organisation asking for his expertise and service. He was on the Boards of Management of the Derbyshire Royal Infirmary and the Nightingale Nursing Home, a Member of the Derby Borough Council Education Committee, served on the Educational Committee of the BBC Midland Section, and was a Governor of Spondon House School. Other local interests were the Derby Society of Engineers, and the Derby Gas Company. Sir Henry additionally practised as a Justice of the Peace on the Derby bench, as had Lady Emma since 1925. Eric, the younger son, still at Oundle preparing for Cambridge, may well have been influenced by the JP status of his parents to consider Law as a career, which he eventually took up.

Further involvements covered such organisations as the YMCA, the Scout movement, The Railway Servants Orphanage and the UK Railway Temperance Union, this last fully in keeping with his lifelong abstinence from alcohol.

By the mid-1920s, Harry Fowler had recovered from the worst effects of his shell-shock and had met and married his wife Edith. Sir Henry and Lady Emma were delighted with this match, seeing it as a sign of Harry's recovery. They were even more delighted when in 1929 Harry and Edith produced a daughter, Jenifer, who was to be their only grandchild in their lifetimes.

Sir Henry, as he grew older, found golf a sport he could take up to fill the void left by the cessation of the more energetic pursuits he enjoyed. He joined the Chevin Golf Club at Duffield, to the north of Derby and could be found there some weekends, busily engaged in playing a round. He was noted for his absence from the 19th hole, in keeping with his abstinence mentioned before. In the 1920s and 1930s, Eric often accompanied him, the pair of them arriving with their clubs in the Armstrong Siddeley saloon.

1930 was the final year of Sir Henry's time as CME, and it is around this time that we get a hint of his realisation that something needed to be done to eradicate once and for all the opposing thoughts on the locomotive design side. In early April of that year he attended a conference of working directors, managers, foremen and forewomen, held at Oxford. He had been invited to speak at this event.

The report of his comments at Oxford is interesting, in that he stated forcefully that to obtain better promotion and acceptance of progressive ideas in industry it was sometimes necessary to break down a natural jealousy, sometimes existing in the engineering sphere between different factions. It is clear from these remarks that he did realise that strong partisanship such as was evident in the Derby design offices needed attention. Whether he himself could deal with this is the crucial point, his own particular engineering philosophy was, naturally, steeped in MR experiences and methodology. Perhaps, around this time he was beginning to think about moving aside for a new CME who would not feel hampered in asserting his authority firmly on the design team. He, himself, had watched for so long as first Horwich under Hughes, then Derby under himself, tried to place their authority on locomotive matters, with some input from Crewe to compound the arguments. Never wanting to 'rock the boat' too much, he had soft-pedalled any criticism, and accepted in the main what was offered by his chief draughtsmen. After all, he is recorded as having said that he never actually *designed* a locomotive. Not a surprising remark, for few CME's ever did. With so strong a representation of the MR at Board level and Anderson having his elevated status as Motive Power Superintendent, matters could well have degenerated into some rather awkward arguments but for the diplomatic handling of affairs by Fowler. So far, his organisational skills had kept production rates at a level sufficient to maintain delivery of new locomotives as required, with the majority of these locomotives being only of moderate size and power, and hence inexpensive. However, putting capital cost on one side, the large recourse to double-heading still to be found all over the LMS rather upset matters in terms of operating cost and, ultimately, repair costs. With his bias towards the research side of things, Henry Fowler may well have tended to gloss over the more practical operational side. He certainly had no jurisdiction over those matters, the 1910 edict of the MR Board had effectively removed that from the CME's remit, and of course the Operating Superintendentcy had been long held by Anderson, someone well steeped in the small engine philosophy.

In July 1929, Eric left Oundle, having achieved much academically and in the sporting activities whilst there. He had won his School Colours for his performances as full back in the Rugby XV, House Colours as a hurdler and been Head of his House, New House. In addition he had been a school prefect. His next academic exercise was to be at Clare College, Cambridge. Sir Henry and Lady Emma were justly proud of their younger son's achievements thus far.

As well as his memberships of the British engineering institutions, Sir Henry, when the occasion permitted, was in touch with several foreign equivalents. One such organisation was the Société des Ingeneurs Francais, for whom he organised a visit to Derby locomotive works. He issued a memorandum to the departments under him asking for volunteers with a reasonable knowledge of French to act as guides. In addition, upon learning that Symes' chief clerk, Whiteside, was fairly fluent in French, he arranged for a guidebook to be written and printed in that language.

Chapter Ten

Experiments and the Final Offerings

The first three events to be described here actually overlap much of the previous Chapter, but are best dealt with as a separate entity in view of their radical approaches to locomotive technology. Henry Fowler, we have seen, was always ready to accept challenges in a research context. It was still one of his main interests.

It was natural, therefore, that he should be intrigued by a proposal by Beyer, Peacock & Co. for the employment of turbine power for steam locomotives. Steam turbine technology was well advanced and had been well proven in shipping for some decades now, but had one drawback, this being that the need to condense the exhaust steam as consistent with shipping installations. The resulting condensing gear required a bulky and heavy tender to accommodate it, and the resulting locomotive was weighty and lengthy. The non-condensing turbine had yet to be developed in a locomotive context.

The system chosen by Beyer, Peacock was the Swedish Ljungstrom principle and, in conjunction with the Swedish inventors, they built a prototype locomotive. Fowler arranged for this to be used on the LMS in 1927, in ordinary revenue-earning service between St Pancras and Manchester. He took a considerable interest in these trials, in which the locomotive performed quite reliably despite its unorthodox power train. However, the LMS was not persuaded to place any investment into furthering turbine power at this time and eventually the engine was returned to Beyer, Peacock. It was to remain for Stanier to introduce the steam turbine on the LMS in the 1930s.

There was a small design study carried out in 1927 involving a possible requirement for an auto-train power unit, comprising a 2-4-0T with a water-tube boiler. Little data on this has survived, apart from a drawing of the chassis. The boiler drawings have not been located, but this would probably have been proposed for supply from one of the more specialist concerns such as the Superheater Company.

Fowler still hankered after some radical developments in the steam locomotive, and his attention was drawn to some work in Germany by Dr Wilhelm Schmidt, the inventor of the firetube superheater. A short time previously, the Institute of Locomotive Engineers had arranged a trip to Germany for some of its members. This was their first trip to this country and proved of great interest to those who went. The party was entertained by the Reichsbahn and commenced with a visit to the Schwenke workshops where the Belt system, as used at Crewe was very much in evidence. They continued to the Henschel factory at Cassel where they saw the Schmidt high pressure boiler locomotive, then undergoing some trials, before being conducted round the nearby State running sheds, which were full of the new massive 2-10-0s then in mass production. Berlin was the next stop on this full agenda, where the party visited the Grunewald test plant. It was here that the results of the tests on the Schmidt high pressure locomotive were presented. A staggering 1.94 lb. per drawbar horsepower being quoted as the measured coal consumption. Dr Wagner, the Reichsbahn CME, one of their hosts, proudly gave this statistic in his usual impeccable English. Sir Henry was not recorded as being at this particular venue, but Symes was there and clearly brought this figure home to Derby.

The Beyer, Peacock-built prototype locomotive built to the Ljungstrom principle. This locomotive was used on the LMS in 1927 in ordinary revenue-earning service between St Pancras and Manchester.

Locomotive Publishing Co.

Fury stored in the Derby Works paint shop, 1932.   *H.F. Wheeller Collection*

The Schmidt proposal was to produce steam at a very high pressure, not through the boiler being in contact with the heat of the firebox or firetubes, but by a closed circuit of distilled water vapourised in what was essentially a water-tube boiler. This operated at a pressure of 1,400 to 1,800 psi, and the high-pressure steam produced thus circulated through a series of coils in a high pressure boiler to produce steam at 900 to 1,000 psi. There was also a conventional boiler heated by firetubes fed from a combustion chamber at the front end of the furnace used to heat the high pressure steam. The concept was to use the high pressure boiler to feed steam to one inside cylinder, the exhaust of which was mixed with steam at 250 psi from the conventional boiler, which then went to the two outside cylinders.

Representatives of the Superheater Company had seen the prototype locomotive using these principles at the 1925 Munich Railway Exhibition and obtained a licence from the holders of the rights, the Schmidt'sche Heissdampf Gesellschaft, to build a locomotive in Great Britain.

Talks between the LMS CME's department, stimulated by the reports brought back from Germany, and the Superheater Company and the North British Locomotive Company resulted in a tripartite agreement to construct a prototype. It was known that Gresley, on the LNER, was involved in a high-pressure exercise to emerge in 1929 as the 4-6-4 No. 10000, with a water-tube boiler pressed to 450 psi. The LMS Board were keen to be seen following technological advances, it was all good publicity. Therefore it was not too difficult for Fowler to obtain the necessary funds to support the research programme.

The boiler design and construction was to be the responsibility of the Superheater Company, the chassis and rest of the locomotive was virtually a standard LMS 'Royal Scot' apart from the cylinder sizes. Assembly was to be carried out at the North British works in Glasgow, whilst the LMS agreed to place an official order for: 'One 4-6-0 Passenger Engine (no tender) Royal Scot class. Fitted with High Pressure Boiler in accordance with the Superheater Company's design, now on order under D3745. General Conditions of L.M. & Scottish specification to offer'.

Henry Fowler had been led to expect considerable economies in fuel consumption and also in time spent on maintenance and repair. How the latter argument ever got accepted is a mystery for so radical a departure from a conventional design. The acceptance of his senior staff's judgement on those matters did him no good, and the events that followed, although never stated as being the catalyst, might well have been one of the features which influenced matters leading to his eventual displacement from office.

Construction of the experimental locomotive proceeded quickly, in accordance with the normal North British habit, and on 6th December, 1929, *Fury*, as it had been named, was fired up for the first time. Many minor problems having been ironed out over some eight or nine weeks, the engine was moved to Polmadie Shed to prepare for some trials on the main line as far as Carstairs.

On the first trial run, the destination was reached with all pressures seemingly operating normally when, as it ran through the station at Carstairs, there was a huge rush of steam from the firebox. One of the 1,800 psi tubes had burst and steam blew the fire out onto the footplate. One of the party of four present on the footplate, a Mr Schofield of the Superheater Company, was fatally injured.

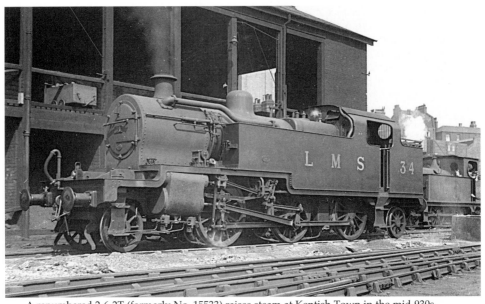

A renumbered 2-6-2T (formerly No. 15533) raises steam at Kentish Town in the mid-930s.
John Scott-Morgan Collection

Fowler 2-6-2T No. 15538 in Derby paint shop. This was one of the condensing batch for work out of Farringdon Street. The appendage by the smokebox is a Weir feed-water pump.
R.S. Carpenter Collection

Experimental 4-6-0 *Fury*. A rare shot of this locomotive in steam. This is dated October 1931, so Lemon must have ordered it out for some trials. The indicator shelters being fitted shows some degree of interest in the tests. The location is not stated, but could be Derby, for that was where the locomotive was stored after the tragedy. *John Scott-Morgan Collection*

The engine was subsequently repaired and then towed to Derby works. After about three years it did go through a few trials authorised by Stanier, although there is photographic evidence that E.J.H. Lemon, in his year as CME in 1931, did order steam raised for some tentative trials. However, by the time of Stanier's trials, a further locomotive utilising the same principle had suffered a similar failure (thankfully without any injuries) in France and the German example had failed to show any fuel economies. The concept thus died and no more ultra high pressure locomotives were to appear in the UK. Gresley's attempt on the LNER also proved rather unreliable, being rebuilt in 1935 with a conventional boiler.

By the time the further testing took place, Fowler was now retired, so any impetus for modifications to improve matters had gone. *Fury* was rebuilt by Stanier with his taper boiler and 'Royal Scot' cylinders and became the prototype for the subsequent rebuilding of that class in later years.

Earlier, in 1928, the LDO had become so crowded that a move to a separate building adjacent to the main office block took place. Alongside this reorganisation Sir Henry, whose external interests still abounded, promoted Symes from Works Superintendent to be his Personal Assistant. The Assistant Locomotive Superintendent at Stoke, H.G. Ivatt, was brought in to take his place. Ivatt was the son of Henry Ivatt, of Great Northern fame, and was eventually to reach the position of CME on the LMS in later years. He had Robin Riddles as his Assistant, and together they transformed the locomotive repair work at Derby into a vastly improved system, such that the number of engines awaiting repair was reduced from 150 to 60. Henry ordered that they be given a free hand and he was heard to remark one day as he was making one of his regular trips around the works: 'This place alters while I go through it!'

Sir Henry clearly got on very well with Ivatt who, on one occasion, drew him into a discussion around some modifications to the Walschaerts valve gear of the 2-6-4 tanks. He listened carefully to Ivatt's explanation, only to floor him with the casual remark: 'Quite honestly, I don't understand the thing!'

Once settled into their new offices, the LDO were ordered to carry out some studies for a tank locomotive to be used on light suburban passenger work. As some staff at Derby had been absorbed from the former NSR office at Stoke, some schemes around the 0-6-2T designed there were drawn up, in addition to further variations of the old MR 0-6-4T.

The 0-6-2T got to the stage of being ordered, but was speedily cancelled, a 2-6-2T layout done in conjunction with the other schemes actually being chosen

Compound No. 1048, built at Derby in 1925, takes a breather after hauling an excursion special to Scarborough in 1930. Note the Gresley 'D49/4' class 4-4-0 in the background with R.C. poppet valves.   *John Scott-Morgan Collection*

The standard 0-6-0T was also supplied to the S&D. A batch of seven being built by Bagnall in 1928. Here No. 22 of that batch is pictured at Radstock in 1930.   *R.S. Carpenter Collection*

for production. Although 70 were eventually built, they were under-boilered and the reversion to short travel valves hampered free running. It seemed that the merits of the 2-6-0, 2-6-4T and 'Royal Scot' with their long travel valves were completely ignored, old Derby practices still wormed their way into the designs. Sir Henry was clearly out of touch with events. He had, for some time now, an office at the Euston HQ of the LMS to which he removed himself quite often. This was handy for his I.Mech.E. and I.Civil E. responsibilities and meetings, but did mean that control of design matters was not completely in his hands. It therefore was not surprising that matters slipped back to old practices of Midland origin. A new broom was needed to sweep away that which prevented the incorporation of all the best in locomotive design. Feelings in the Derby-Horwich-Crewe triangle still stood high and, at last, it appeared that the LMS Board recognised that something had to be done.

As events started moving towards Fowler's change of responsibility, a further batch of 'Royal Scots', which had certainly proved themselves as reliable and powerful locomotives, was ordered. Derby works turned out the 20 authorised - the first production run of large express locomotives to emerge from these works. H.G. Ivatt was responsible for organising the production, the first of the batch being laid down on 5th May and completed and ready for traffic on 31st May.

There is a story concerning this batch of the 'Royal Scots' in that originally, they were costed at £7,350 each, minus tender. This cost, however was based on a erroneous calculation, having been based on a cost per ton *including* tender weight. Fowler was, to put it mildly, a bit dismayed at this basic error having been made and called in Ivatt to explain the predicament. Ivatt promised to do his best to reduce costs where possible and actually succeeded, to Sir Henry's great relief, in matching this cost.

Throughout his CME days, Fowler was noted for a close interest in boiler design. It is recorded (*Railway Magazine,* Sept. and Oct. 1942) that towards the end of his LMS tenure he ordered that a boiler suit be kept available at some of the sheds he visited on his inspection tours. Upon reaching the relevant shed he would first ascertain the status of the locomotives under repair and then select one for a close examination. This resulted in the boiler suit being donned and him entering the firebox with a torch, hammer, piece of chalk and a 'volunteer' helper. The staff present always marvelled at the way in which he got his substantial frame through the tight confines of the fire-door. He would then proceed to use the hammer to tap at the firebox staybolts, marking any he thought might be defective or loose for further inspection and rectification. The willingness to enter such a confined space and not worry about his appearance in this 'hands-on' approach endeared him to many of the shed staff, despite the resulting minor disruption to the maintenance schedules. 'E's great on boilers, is Sir 'Enry' was one typical comment.

Back in 1927, Fowler had, as a temporary expedient, 20 of the ex-LNWR 'Claughtons' reboiled, which markedly improved their performance. However, they still retained many of the adverse features which were accentuated by the difficulty in adequately reaching some components for even basic maintenance. Clearly some drastic changes were needed to make this locomotive acceptable, if it were to remain in traffic. And thus it was that the final locomotive design to appear under Fowler was the 'rebuilding' of some of

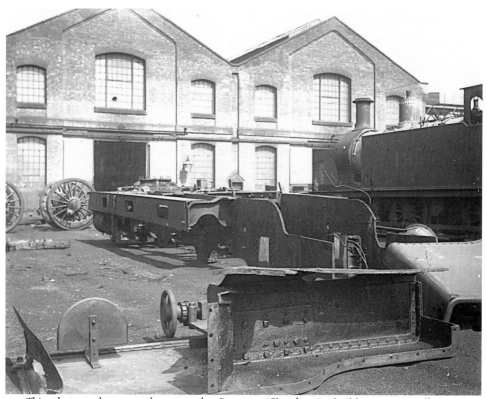

This photograph proves that even the first two 'Claughton' rebuilds were virtually new throughout. Here are the remains of No. 5971 are being cut up outside Derby works in 1930.

R.S. Carpenter Collection

No. 5971 as reborn in 'Baby Scot' guise.   *R.S. Carpenter Collection*

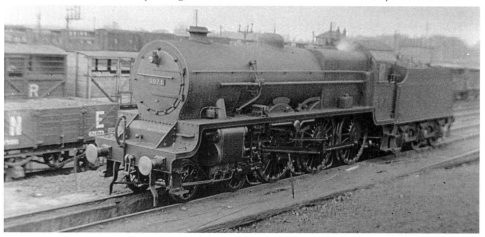

the LNWR 'Claughton' 4-6-0s. Although listed as rebuilds, this was more for accountancy reasons than anything else. Essentially this design was an enlarged Claughton boiler on a 'Royal Scot' chassis. Two were built in November 1930, just before Sir Henry was moved to the rôle of Assistant for research matters to Sir Harold Hartley, who had recently joined the Euston management team.

Forty of the 'rebuilt' 'Claughtons' were dealt with at their progenitor's birthplace, Crewe, the class totalling some 52 at the finish. Again, the use of the long travel valves as on the 'Royal Scot', produced a fine locomotive, and the lives of these engines were extended to the end of steam on BR. The 50 to come after the successful introduction of the initial two were, in fact, completely new locomotives, as when Lemon took office as CME in 1931, one of the first orders he gave was to have the whole class examined. As a result of the report that ensued it was resolved to make the next 50 locomotives entirely new rather than convert the existing class members. Not even the wheels, bogies and sundry fittings, as used on the first two, were to be retained.

Other sections of the LDO were kept busy in 1930 in studies for more tank engines. An 0-8-4T was drawn up, probably for hump shunting. No drawings remain but this design was to have 20 inch diameter cylinders with 26 inch stroke and a 200 lb./sq. in. boiler. This design could have had some common features with the '7F' 0-8-0 and been a tank version of that design. It never went further than this study. A second tank type was also schemed for light mixed traffic work, this being an 0-4-4T which got much further, some detail parts being drawn up before being put on one side, and was to be resurrected the next year in the latter days of Lemon's time as CME.

One further small production exercise as Sir Henry prepared to depart the scene was the provision of a further batch of ten 4-4-2Ts for the ex-LT&SR lines. Commuter traffic into London was heavy and additional locomotives were needed to enable services to be maintained at their high level. But even these old designs, updated though they were, struggled with the increasing weight of commuter trains on that busy line. The 2-6-4T would have been an ideal choice, and that in fact is precisely what Stanier produced to alleviate the situation once he took office as CME in the early 1930s.

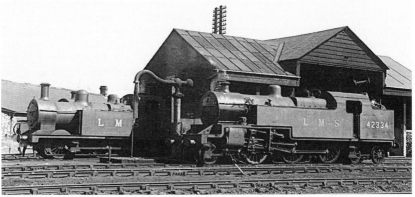

Fowler 2-6-4T in later LMS livery and numbering sits at the coaling stage at St Albans in 1949. Although this was early BR days, the scene is typical LMS, particularly with the 'Jinty' 0-6-0T beside it.   *John Scott-Morgan Collection*

Chapter Eleven

Research and the Approach of Retirement

By 1930, the President of the LMS, Sir Josiah Stamp, had weighed up the situation regarding the CME's department and decided that a change was needed. Fowler still held the post, but his grip on matters was not enough to implement the radical change clearly needed. His handling of matters over the previous six years had only spasmodically produced locomotives employing the latest in design thinking. Too much reliance on old methodology and traits was evident. Beames still resided at Crewe, and was thought by some as being the logical replacement for Fowler, but this would only bring Crewe ideas to the fore and the rivalries would continue. So, realising this, Stamp started casting around outside for a replacement CME. Meantime, how to handle matters diplomatically was his top priority for, despite his shortcomings, Fowler had run matters efficiently at the expense of bowing to Derby practices. This was perfectly natural, for he had been established there for 30 years and was well versed in handling an experienced team through his deputies. It was too late for him to change.

The previous year, Stamp had invited Sir Harold Hartley to accept the post of Vice-President and Director of Scientific Research. The key factor precipitating this change at the top was the sudden death, in March 1929, of R.W. Reid who, in 1927, had been plucked by Stamp from his position as Carriage and Wagon Engineer at Derby and placed at Euston as Vice-President Mechanical Engineering. The position had to be filled and Stamp took advantage of the situation to rename the job in favour of the research title. A Fellow of the Royal Society and, since 1901, a Fellow and Tutor of Balliol College, Oxford, Hartley brought an independent mind to research on the railway, taking up his responsibilities on 1st January, 1930. He had, of course, no previous experience on railway matters and clearly needed someone in the capacity of an assistant to advise, in particular, on mechanical engineering matters. Someone sufficiently high enough and experienced to command respect throughout the railway scenario. The opportunity presented itself for Stamp to suggest diplomatically to Sir Henry Fowler that here was a challenging job for him to take up as he approached retirement. The date for the change-over was set for 31st December, 1930.

This, certainly, was a sideways move, or as some of the technical staff called it, a 'shunt', but Fowler was not the sort to hold a grudge against his superiors. The opportunity to continue in office outweighed his disappointment at the undoubted snub. He clearly saw himself as being capable of going on for some considerable time. His energy was still unbounded, even though he was in his sixties, still occasionally playing cricket for Spondon during the summer. Also, the tantalising chance to indulge in one of his favourite engineering aspects, that of research, spurred him on to accept this position of Assistant to the Vice-President. He would be close to the top management and, being frequently in London, fully able to keep in touch with the Institutions of which he was a member. The office at Euston was for decision making only, for the big task allotted to him, at the start of his tenure, was to set up a Research Laboratory at Derby. This suited him as he was frequently up where he felt happy, in and around that town. Also, by 1931, Emma was not in the best of health, so he could be around much of the time to comfort her. Dorothea, now in her twenties, dutifully stayed at home to support her parents.

Sir Henry settled into his new position quite happily and started building up what was to become a long-lasting and excellent research centre at Derby, which continued into BR days. His remit from Hartley was firstly to take control of the chemical and paint laboratories and the beginnings of an engineering section and to co-ordinate them into an independent research department of the LMS. He also formed teams to staff metallurgical and textile laboratories. He ordered that the major metallurgical matters should be covered under three headings, the wear of tyres and rails, stresses in tyres, and locomotive springing. The emphasis on tyres was because he was acutely aware that the Lytham accident of 1927 was caused by a worn tyre fracturing and thus considerable research was obviously needed. His specialised metallurgical interests were aroused, leading to some more research into the effects of certain tool materials on the machining of tyres. The net result of this research was that the original high-speed steel tools were substituted for carbide steel tools under Stanier shortly after he took over as CME. In the materials context, in earlier years, Fowler had investigated the use of carbon steel cold chisels which tended to crack due to heavy use and introduced nickel-steel replacements which were better and also capable of being sharpened with a file.

Sir Harold Hartley looked around with an outsider's eyes and saw a huge number of different classes of locomotives, hardly a recipe for economic operation. The infighting between the various factions had completely negated any attempt to produce a reasonable number of 'standard' classes to alleviate the high cost of supporting so many classes. Considerable economies had been made in the works area, but so far as getting the fleet into order, little could be seen as accomplished. Hartley had no special leaning towards any of the myriad designs in service and, from a dispassionate point of view, determined that when he had absorbed the situation some drastic action would be taken to remedy matters.

Initially, for a year's term, E.J.H. Lemon was put in as CME at Euston. Lemon immediately placed Beames in charge as Deputy CME, at Derby, on the understanding that this was purely a holding operation, for Lemon was destined for higher office very soon. Hartley looked around and pondered where he might find a suitable successor, discussing matters with Lemon in the meantime.

As a member of the Permanent Commission to the International Railway Congress, Sir Henry felt duty bound to be involved in the sessions. He made a point of preparing a paper for delivery whenever possible. The Madrid IRC in 1930 was a case in point, with a joint presentation on the static and dynamic stresses in railway bridges. This he researched in collaboration with George Ellson, the Chief Civil Engineer of the Southern Railway. Ellson had recently recovered from a nervous breakdown caused by the extreme pressures on him following the Sevenoaks derailment in which 13 died. This accident was blamed on locomotive instability caused by inadequate drainage of the track causing it to sink under load. He had been ordered to implement the complete overhaul of the Southern tracks to bring them to an acceptable standard, the workload and responsibilities for this had precipitated his illness. With this joint paper he was to demonstrate his full recovery and continued in office for many years.

Sir Henry and brother Alex at niece Katherine's (Molly's daughter) wedding, 14th May, 1931.

Mrs D. Fowler

Lady Emma and Sir Henry with son Eric, following his graduation from Clare College, Cambridge.

Mrs D. Fowler

So far as non-railway interests were concerned, in the 1931 County Council elections for Derbyshire, Sir Henry entered the political fray as an Independent, but failed to win the seat by 144 votes. He had decided to stand as an Independent not wishing to align himself with any of the major parties with whom he could not find much common ground. He was, according to Lady Emma, rather disappointed at his failure to get elected, but soon the research tasks took over and he was busy preparing for a business trip to Berlin.

About three weeks after his German visit Sir Henry, accompanied by Lady Emma, paid a visit to Evesham and his parents' grave. He was clearly much attached to the town of his birth and made this pilgrimage on an annual basis, sometimes staying over a weekend with his brother Charles who still ran the family furniture and upholstery shop, H. Fowler and Sons, in the High Street.

The Institute of Metals arranged its 1931 conference in Zurich and Henry arranged to attend, with Emma accompanying him. Friday, 4th September found them crossing the Channel *en route* to Switzerland, arriving in Zurich early the following morning. The proceedings commenced on Sunday evening and Henry spent most of the week at meetings whilst Emma enjoyed the many sightseeing trips arranged for the wives. One high spot was a trip to Lucerne on the 12th September, where they went up one of the nearby mountains for lunch at 6,000 ft. Emma obviously enjoyed this trip, it was to be her last outside of the UK, and noted in her diary for the 17th September: 'Home, after a most delightful and happy holiday'. She returned to her Magisterial and other tasks refreshed and invigorated by this time abroad. We find a most interesting entry in the diary concerning a Court hearing at which one particular person was fined £10 10s. for: 'larceny (petrol) and for taking a car for *joy riding*'. Is this one of the earliest recorded uses of this phrase for a now commonplace crime?

This particular year Dorothea travelled to Cambridge to partner Eric at the Clare College Summer ball, on the 15th June. Whether Eric had designs on getting his sister to meet a suitable companion amongst his many friends is not known, but if so, this did not materialise then. She was content to be at home to care for her parents so far.

The 10th August found Sir Henry *en route* to Paris for a research meeting, returning home to Spondon on the 14th.

One of the many organisations benefitting from the Fowler's patronage was the Temperance Society. The 1931 Bazaar of the Derby branch was held on the 4th October and this year was opened by Lady Stamp, wife of Sir Josiah Stamp, himself being a life-long teetotaller like Sir Henry.

Christmas 1931 at Spondon Hall was as usual, a great family affair. The eldest son Harry with wife Edith and daughter Jenifer arrived to stay, and with Eric home from Cambridge and Dorothea in residence, the Fowlers were complete as a family for a few days.

Towards the end of 1931, as Henry Fowler started to build up his research team and facilities at Derby, some crucial meetings took place in London concerning a new CME for the LMS. Initially, Hartley and Lemon were drawn to Swindon, which had after all been the catalyst for the emergence of the 'Royal Scot', certainly the most successful express locomotive on the LMS, and to William Stanier in particular, who was then Principal Assistant to the GWR Chief Mechanical Engineer, C.B. Collett.

William A. Stanier.   *National Railway Museum*

Accordingly, in January 1932, Stanier took over as the new CME of the LMS. The old Derby order of short travel valves and small to medium sized engines was swept aside to be replaced with all the best of Swindon, although, it should be said the Swindon low superheat practice was quickly diagnosed as being inappropriate and the high degree LMS practice adopted. Stanier established his team at Euston and thus broke the direct link to the old-established partisan practices when Derby reigned supreme.

To complement his research work, Sir Henry Fowler was appointed by the International Railway Congress Association as one of three special reporters. The task of these reporters was to investigate 'Methods to be used to increase the mileage run by locomotives between two repairs, including lifting'. They were asked to present their findings at the forthcoming IRC to be held in Cairo. Fowler, and one of his co-reporters, came to the conclusion that the limiting factor was predominantly the boiler, and thus more research should be put into extending boiler life, either by improved materials or methods of construction.

1932 was to be his final year of service for the LMS. Emma's health was a concern, although she dutifully carried on her civic reponsibilities with great faithfulness. But it is noticeable from her diaries that quite a few engagements had to be cancelled at fairly short notice. It was this year that we find her making several recuperative visits to Southbourne, sometimes in the company of Dorothea. On some of these visits they would drive over to Bosham to visit Henry's sister Jeannie, who lived there and still practised as a nurse.

It is noticeable that Henry's concern for Emma was growing, this comes out in many of his letters written this year and, clearly, the situation must have had an impact on his decision to retire fairly soon.

In 1932, Sir Henry paid two visits to Germany in connection with his research position at Euston. In June the task was to assess some developments in locomotive technology, for the Germans were at that time engaged in developing diesel power and the LMS was interested in finding out more about this, and had in fact commenced to experiment with a diesel-hydraulic locomotive at Derby. Fowler was given a ride on one of the development trains. His command of the German language was not at all good and some advice as how to manage a friendly manner from son Harry was tried out:

I am now on my own, I was going to say at last, for the trial train they arranged for me brought me to within an hour of here. [He wrote from Halberstadt, continuing] I had quite an affecting parting with Dr Wagner (Chief of the Mechanical Section of the German State Railways) as I told him that it was questionable if I should come over again officially - Harry wrote truer than he probably knew when he wrote 'smile' for I have been smiling my way on to this train as well as trying to smile a paper pad from the fellow at the bookstall - but he had not got one or I would have done so. Why I had to smile my way into the train is that I am going, all being well, to Quedlinberg. This is the town at which when in the Finkenhead catching finches, they came and told Henry the Fowler that he was Emperor of Germany. Yesterday Dr Kühne got it into his head that I had relatives there . . .

he wrote to Emma on the 28th June.

Later, in the same letter he added some comments on Quedlinberg: '. . . but although my name is right I do not suppose they will make me Emperor at Quedlinberg. I don't know that I want them to!'

Smoke deflection developments on the 'Royal Scot' started with some rather unsightly shields beside the chimney. Here No. 6133 *Vulcan* is caught at Crewe North Shed in *c.* 1932.

R.S. Carpenter Collection

The more effective smoke deflector, with straight panels. No. 6126 leaves Crewe on an up express. Note how the exhaust is still entrained at the front of the chimney. Clearly a further modification is needed.   *R.S. Carpenter Collection*

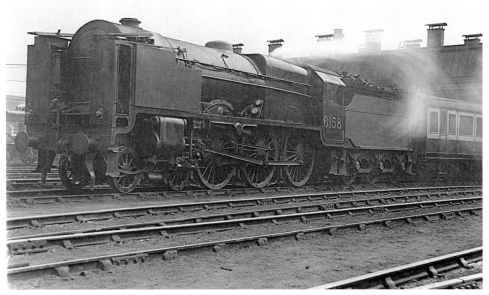

As Fowler retired, more trials were carried out on the 'Royal Scot' No. 6158 of the Derby batch. The ex-LNWR dynamometer car being used. Here the locomotive is found at Crewe North Shed, ready for these trials in April 1933. *A.V.W. Mace Collection*

The final smoke deflector shape, cranked in at the top. No. 6123 *Royal Irish Fusilier* at Crewe North in 1937. By this time several of the class had been paired with Stanier tenders much more in keeping with the size of the locomotive. *R.S. Carpenter Collection*

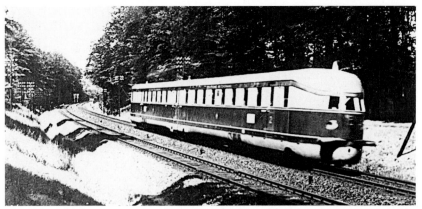

The German high speed diesel multiple unit 'The Flying Hamburger'.

John Alsop Collection

Obviously the old town near the Harz mountains struck him as being worthy of a visit and he concluded:

> If being Emperor meant being boss of this little town I don't know if I would not take it on. I wonder that folks don't visit it from all over the world. It's old houses and quaint streets, its Rathaus and, above all, its Church and Schloss-on-a-rock. The Hartz [*sic*] mountains and the Brocken in the distance. But, oh the cobbles and my poor feet!

The political situation in Germany was, in 1932, very fluid. No fewer than five general elections were held that year, as the Nazi party slowly increased its influence on affairs of state. With each election, although their number of seats fluctuated up and down, the influence of Hitler and his henchmen was growing and he was, in a few months, to manipulate matters such that he was proclaimed Chancellor. Obviously, Sir Henry enjoyed his June trip to Germany, but one senses a definite change in matters as the Nazis grew in influence. In November, during a subsequent visit, he wrote from the Palast Hotel, Dusseldorf: 'I am shortly going in a car to Bochum further north. I was well received and looked after yesterday by Professor Körber, who gave the "Metals" lecture last year, and a Dr Petersen who I had an introduction to. I did not get any very definite information, but lots of negative'.

No further visits to Germany were made as the iron grip of the Nazis took hold, although he frequently travelled to other European countries.

Before he left for Germany on this final visit, Henry, mindful that the first day of his journeying would be Emma's birthday, the 1st November, bought a couple of gifts and arranged for them to be delivered to Spondon Hall. He wrote a short covering note to accompany them, which included the customary comment on her 21st: 'How well I remember your 21st and how I shall think of it tomorrow'.

In between the German trips there was a flurry of travel, firstly a short visit to Brussels via the Euston head office of the LMS, followed by attendance at an Oxford conference and finally a last business trip to Paris.

The honours continued to pile up, for in 1932, Sir Henry was elected to the Presidency of the Institute of Metals. This pleased him considerably and it recognised his contributions to metallurgy from the research carried out on the railways over the years. The Institution of Mechanical Engineers also bestowed on him an Honorary Life Membership, a status only reserved for the most famous of engineers.

Meantime, up at Derby, whilst the research department continued to grow under Fowler's energetic leadership, he realised that he would never again hold such a powerful hand as he had in his earlier CME days. He still had plenty of outside interests, particularly as the Ministry of Transport were keen on obtaining his services as Chairman of a new Committee to be given the task of investigating means of restricting noise from road traffic, now growing at a considerable rate.

At the end of 1932, Sir Henry Fowler resigned from the LMS, in order to devote himself more fully to his Ministry of Transport part-time chairmanship and additionally be at home more often, for Emma's health was far from robust. Eric had now graduated from Cambridge and returned to Derby and joined the local Police Force as a constable, to gain firsthand experience to assist his desire to enter the legal profession. He sometimes could be found on point duty in Derby, and it is on record that at least once he held up his father when driving through the town. A reporter from Derby witnessed one such event and it made a short piece of news in the following edition of the *Derby Daily Telegraph*, for the Fowlers were obviously well known and respected locally.

A month after Eric had commenced his police duties, he was suddenly struck down with acute appendicitis, necessitating an emergency operation followed by three weeks recuperation. Once home at Spondon Hall from hospital, he took advantage of his enforced inactivity to search for a flat in Derby as he felt he would like to be nearer his place of employment with its sometimes unsocial hours of duty. In this he was successful and on 31st October moved into a flat at No. 4 Hartington Street. Sir Henry and Lady Emma saw him settled in and returned to Spondon Hall and the company of Dorothea.

Whilst he was living in Derby and employed by the Derby Police, Eric was much in demand to act as MC at the dances held in and around Spondon. He was only too happy to oblige, having his father's cheerful, outgoing, temperament. 'A chip off the old block' was an apt description of his social ways.

The Fowler expertise in locomotive design lived on in Northern Ireland after his retirement, for in 1933 a batch of four 2-6-0 tender locomotives was turned out at Derby to meet the demand of the NCC for a modern mixed traffic type. These were derived from the 2-6-4T introduced in 1927, and still in production. These NCC locomotives had the long travel, long lap valve gear of the tank type and were so well received and successful that a further 11 examples were to be built in Belfast from parts manufactured by Derby and Crewe. Finally, in 1945, some 2-6-4Ts were built for the NCC, the design being very similar to Fowler's own, subject to changes made by Stanier and Fairburn in later years. No fewer than 18 of these tanks were constructed at Derby for this arm of the LMS, some of which were to be the last working steam locomotives in the UK (other than those preserved) only ceasing regular operation in May 1970. Sir Henry would have been well satisfied with the length of service of these locomotives derived from those designed under his leadership all those years ago.

The NCC 2-6-0, derived from Fowler's 2-6-4T at York Road, Belfast on 6th June, 1953. Note the Fowler standard tender supplied with these. The coach in view is also standard LMS on 5 ft 3 in. bogies.   *R.G. Jarvis Collection, MRT*

The NCC 2-6-4T, designed under Ivatt in 1946 in process of erection at Derby. The design was based on the Fowler 2-6-4T to allow for commonality with the earlier 2-6-0 tender locomotives.
Derby Industrial Museum

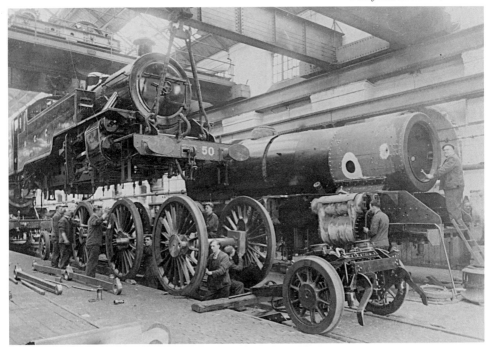

Chapter Twelve

Retirement and the Cairo Congress

As 1932 drew to a close, Sir Henry gradually handed over his research duties to his principal assistants and began preparing for his forthcoming trip to the 1933 International Railway Congress which was to have its next gathering in Cairo. At this he was due to report his findings in the capacity as a Special Reporter on locomotive mileage between overhaul times, in addition to being the General Secretary of the Congress. Emma was not to be able to accompany him this time as her health was giving cause for concern and she had arranged another visit to Southbourne to relax. Henry also planned to stay on in the Middle East after the Congress to see some of Egypt. This was to be followed by a trip to Palestine to visit an archaeological site in Gaza after which he planned some travels through that country to see some of the places he had read and taught about so much in his Bible Class days.

The trip out to Cairo, in the company of many of the UK delegates to the IRC was on the P&O liner SS *Rawalpindi*, departing on 30th December, 1932, a Friday. This vessel was to come into the headlines in 1939, when as an armed merchant cruiser, she took on the German pocket battleship *Scharnhorst* and cruiser *Gniesenau* and was sunk with dreadful loss of life. The engagement had the result of alerting the British Navy of the presence of the German vessels attempting to break out into the Atlantic convoy lanes and caused them to withdraw to their home port with their cover broken.

By the afternoon of the 31st the ship was negotiating the Bay of Biscay in a gale, as Henry wrote:

> The sea has not been at all kind today and I have been lying in my berth practically all day. I went to the dining room to have lunch and had a piece of toast. Mrs Lemon was the only one at one table. I am hoping it may get better.

He managed to get some sleep that night and continued on New Year's Day:

> It is just after 8.30 am and for the last half hour I have been lying and trying to follow the service with you. I am thinking that you are just on your way down the garden on your way home. The rain has stopped here as I hope it has with you. The sea has gone down but there is a swell at times. It is still cloudy although it was quite clear and the stars were shining during the night. I feel alright lying down but somewhat sore in my tummy, although I was not very sick yesterday. I am going to stay now I am up but do not know if I shall try and dress at present.

It being a Sunday, Henry was determined to get to the publicised service, but the weather had caused so much sea-sickness that no one turned up. He was obviously getting his sea-legs and appetite back, as he continued later: 'I had a nice lunch, soup, custard and cheese. I feel better in the stomach but not happy except when lying down'.

Much of his spare time up to now had been taken up with resting and reading his favourite, the *Times Literary Supplement*, and he closed that Sunday's

One of Sir Henry's photographs, SS *Rawalpindi* at Gibraltar, Tuesday, 3rd January 1933, whilst passengers took a trip ashore.   *Mrs D. Fowler*

The view looking north from Europa Point, Gibraltar, taken by Sir Henry during his trip ashore.
                                                                        Mrs D. Fowler

commentary with: 'The sea went down a bit but is 'lumpy' again. Hope you are enjoying your tea. Should reach the end of the Bay at 7 pm and Gib by 10 Tuesday'.

The *Rawalpindi* was not the smoothest of vessels and Henry was sometimes annoyed by the vibration caused by the rough sea making the screws to break surface occasionally. On the Monday, the storms had abated and the ship was much steadier, so just before lunch he sat down to pen a few more lines to Emma:

> I did not sleep much during the day yesterday, but went to bed early and to sleep at once and so was awake later. I should get normal now. It was much better this morning and I did a dozen walks round the deck and had a game of quoits. Everyone is on deck of our party but Mrs Newlands looks sadly yet and is keeping quiet.

Just before dinner that day, he added the finishing touches to the letter:

> It is right I should finish off my writing to you dearest and I am doing, for I hope to post this before I dress for dinner at 7.30. The dinners are about as the ones we had on the 'Saxon' and not as elaborate as the ones on the Atlantic. There is plenty and no mistake. [continuing later] We ought to see Trafalgar at 7 tomorrow and to be at Gib at 8. We should go ashore for about a couple of hours and I shall try to do so.

Life on board had obviously now returned to normal, as he started to describe some of his fellow passengers:

> There is a fellow on board whose nationality we can't make out. Either a Russian or Pole I think: he says he often comes this way and that we shall be in sight of land nearly all the way from Gib to Marseilles.

They called at Gibraltar, anchoring for a few hours, whilst several passengers took the opportunity of a visit ashore. Sir Henry was one of these, taking his camera to record a view of the Rock from Europa Point and also a good view of the *Rawalpindi* at anchor in the harbour. The next port of call was Marseilles, where Henry went ashore whilst many extra passengers joined the ship, having travelled overland to avoid the winter storms of the Bay of Biscay. They then set sail for Port Said on the Friday evening. By 8.45 pm the following evening Henry went up on deck to find them passing through the Straits of Bonifacio between Corsica and Sardinia after which the course turned south easterly for the Straits of Messina. The passage thus far from Marseilles had only produced one rough patch:

> It has been fine today but got quite rough midday and Mrs Lemon and myself had lunch alone. There was a full table for dinner as I take it we got under the shelter of Corsica.

The following day was a Sunday and Sir Henry attended the 10.45 service in the dining saloon, which was taken by a Revd French, one of the passengers. Good time was being made and in the late afternoon they passed near the Liparii archipilaego with the peak of Stromboli on the port side hidden in the low clouds. Some passengers claimed to have seen a puff of smoke from this, the only regularly active volcano in Europe, but Henry was below at the time. He did, however, record Stromboli on film.

Nearing Sicily, the *Rawalpindi* passed by Stromboli. Any activity is masked by the cloud cover of the crater. Sir Henry obtained this view to record the only regularly active volcano in Europe.
Mrs D. Fowler

An express passenger 4-4-2 locomotive of the Egyptian State Railways at Port Said. It is being made ready to haul a Port Said-Cairo express. This locomotive type was depicted on a special issue Egyptian postage stamp to commemorate the International Railway Congress.
Oakwood Collection

That evening, they passed through the Straits of Messina, and this was described by Sir Henry thus:

> . . . we had what I thought was a very wonderful experience. The rain had cleared up and the moon was out when we got near the Straits of Messina. There seemed towns and lights all along both shores. It was of course (7 pm) dark and the lights were twinkling. We seemed to be going straight for the Italian shore and when, I suppose, ½ to 1 mile off swung sharply round and made for the Sicilian town of Messina. In a little while we turned again and went between the mainland and island which are only 2 miles apart. There is a very strong current through the straits. The towns were very fully lighted as I fancy they do not pay for current but only for how many lights they have.

Monday morning found Sir Henry striding round the deck: 'I have had a good walk, 10 times round (9=1 mile)'. The weather was cold and showery which restricted his exercise and deck games somewhat. By Thursday 10th January, they were off Crete and the passengers for Egypt, including the IRC delegates, were busy packing for disembarkation at Port Said the following day. They left the ship on the morning of 11th January and made their way to the station to catch the train for Cairo.

Henry put the letter describing the voyage from Marseilles in the Air Mail from Cairo and quickly added a final page:

> Egypt 12.45 midday. On train. Here at last and how I wish you could look out of the window with me. There was a very quiet gentleman at Communion on Sunday, but I talked a little with him on the boat. He is sitting opposite me at lunch and has been pointing a lot out to me. He is a Government geologist here 4 months Egypt, 8 months Surrey. I got through Port Said easily thanks to 'Mr Cooks' and the courier without trouble. From Port Said there was desert - just sand - along the canal for a long while. When we turned off we began to get cultivation and donkeys and camels and small irrigation channels. A lot of folks on the land. Houses which do not look finished at the top. I will write more fully later.

This letter posted had the photographs taken on the voyage enclosed. Three of these photographs are to be found illustrating this Chapter.

The train journey to Cairo took four hours, with lunch in the dining car and Sir Henry was clearly much interested in what he saw *en route*, as we have seen in the above extract. He elaborated on the journey in his first letter from the Heliopolis Palace Hotel in Cairo, written on 11th January:

> How can I begin. The whole land is so different to what I have ever seen and yet perhaps not surprising, for one had read about it, and it is much as one has imagined and yet, somewhat different in details. As I said in my hurried note in the train we first travelled through desert by the side of the canal. It was first of all partly covered with shallow (sea) water and then just sand, flat or at the most with low irregularities. After we turned West from the canal at Ismailia we got cultivation and groves of palm trees and unbelievable villages of mud huts none of which looks finished at the top. Flat at the top and often covered with drying maize, which I believe is a danger from fire. There were trees where there was water. Eucalyptus, tamarisk and a tree feathery and like that one in the bed on the lawn near the middle gate, also some acacia. Just before Cairo, thanks to Dr Hume who was very good, I saw in the distance the pyramids for a moment.

The Acting General Manager of the Egyptian Railways sent his secretary to meet the train at Cairo station and Sir Henry found, in addition, three uniformed men and a bus to take him and some of his companions to the Heliopolis Palace Hotel, where many of the British delegates had booked in. This plush establishment certainly impressed him: 'It is some place and no mistake. I have a sitting room as well as other things'.

After unpacking he boarded a tram outside the Hotel to go down to the local office of the IRC to let them know the General Secretary had arrived. He described his journey down town thus:

> I went on an ordinary tram instead of the rapid tram by mistake but was glad for I never saw (nor was I likely to have done) such a collection of folks. They are the same in the streets, men with fez's [sic] and European clothes, men with long 'nightshirts' of various designs, men in divided skirts, men in ordinary skirts. I dare not attempt to describe the women, not many have their faces half covered. I got out by the station and was uncertain where to go . . .

However, an English police sergeant noticed his obvious dilemma and ordered an English speaking Constable to guide him to the street where the office was located: 'It was a long street and I finally found the office and folks I know'.

The following day, Thursday 12th January, was a busy one. Firstly Henry called at the Railway Office to thank the Acting General Manager for his help on arrival. Here he was informed that a Railway Museum was being prepared for opening at the commencement of the Congress and he was taken down to it and given a preview by the Traffic Manager. His reaction to this was included in one of the letters:

> . . . which is really wonderful. The Murdoch locomotive has the place of honour as it ought to have. I have not been able to get in touch with the Chief Mechanical Engineer who is running the Museum - we seem to keep on missing one another. There is a 'Royal Scot' model but somewhat in a corner. The chisels were not placed yet. It is to be opened by the King on Sunday.

The chisels were clearly of the latest type developed from Fowler's recently carried out research into steels. Whilst he had a bit of spare time before the commencement of the Congress, in order to arrange matters for his planned trip to Palestine after the Congress had finished, Henry paid a visit to Cook's, and met the Managing Director, a Mr Baker, who invited him to lunch the following day. Following this he had intended to walk to Old Cairo but got lost, ending up at the Citadel, which he found a good place to view the city from:

> The view from a terrace over the city is wonderful. Just below are two magnificent mosques (or one mosque and a tomb) grand erections, one with a doorway over 50 feet high. The view was not clear but one could see the two pyramids at Gizeh. It was somewhat misty on the ground. It is a marvellous city with old mosques and other buildings and yet with narrow and crowded streets.

From the 14th to the 17th January, Sir Henry was busy organising matters for the forthcoming Congress, spending long hours at the downtown office, meeting delegates off the trains and arranging the opening ceremony which both the British High Commissioner and Egyptian King, Fuad II, were to attend.

On the 17th the weather took a turn for the worse: 'Just England at its very worst, drizzle and rain, rain and drizzle'.

The following morning, a final meeting of the IRC organising commission took place, at which Sir Henry was reappointed Auditor for the next term. After lunch he went again to the Egyptian Museum followed by a call at Shepheard's Hotel to collect a Mr Bover, the Pennsylvania RR representative in London, and they went by tram to the Citadel to climb a minaret to view the city from its 150 ft top gallery and watch the sun set behind the Pyramids. As the sun disappeared from view the report of a gun was heard which showed that the fast was over for the day, it being Ramadan.

The 19th was the formal opening of the Cairo Congress and Henry wrote a graphic account of this to Emma:

> We went down to the Opera cramped up in a bus for the formal opening of the Congress. I thought it was by the King but he only sat in a box where only those on the platform could see him properly. As it happens I was, as a General Secretary, in the front row and sat near him. He is short and stout. The Opera House is a fine building. After the formal opening we British members of the Commission went to the Railway Exhibition at the Museum.

The opening ceremony and Museum visit over, Henry, with Mr Harvey from New Zealand and Mr Swallow from South Africa visited the Arab Museum in the city before viewing the Tombs of the Caliphs on the outskirts. That evening he spent much of his time making some last minute alterations to the opening day's programme of the Congress.

Friday 20th January was the day when the proceedings opened with several sessions. Sir Henry gave his paper that morning: 'It was somewhat tiring with all the translation and of course I had to be there, whereas I ought to have been going round the various sections and seeing how they were going on' he wrote that evening.

The afternoon's excursion for the delegates was a boat trip down the Nile to a barrage near which were some ornate gardens. On their return trip they had a good view of the Pyramids against the setting sun, framed by the riverside palm trees. Sir Henry then relaxed over a quiet dinner that evening.

The next day he was busy from 9.30 am at the Congress, paying special attention to the translation needs of the many foreign delegates, after which he left early as he had a lunch engagement with the High Commissioner at the Residency: 'Evidently they have 10 guests each day. The house has a beautiful garden by the Nile'. He excused himself early from this engagement to join that afternoon's excursion which took in the oldest mosque in Cairo and two old Coptic churches. Immediately after this he went to collect the young son of the Cook's Managing Director, Mr Baker, as he had promised to take him to the Railway Museum: 'He is 7 and was bubbling over with excitement and a very nice little boy'. Henry's enjoyment of this child's company was very evident, and the boy himself was obviously delighted with such a personable and famous engineer to conduct him through the wonders of the railway world displayed in the Museum.

That was not the end of things for this busy day, for after delivering the small boy back to his parents, Henry then returned to the Hotel to inspect and approve the English portion of the Congress Proceedings. With just enough time for his dinner, which tonight he did not enjoy, Sir Henry was then driven to the Palace to be received by the King:

> We specially invited ones were at the Palace at 9 to be received by the King, as we were, well after 9. The nations went in alphabetical order except for our special positions here and we 10, headed by the High Commissioner, marched along most gorgeous rooms, shook hands and passed on through the crowds of ordinary delegates etc.

After the initial formalities they all made their way to a great hall used as a theatre for a performance of the 2nd Act of 'Die Fledermaus' given by some Austrian players and singers, followed by a ballet. The organisation of the Egyptian authorities was clearly not of the highest order but certainly better than the English as: 'when I went for my coat I could not get it and many delegates were the same. It was nothing like as bad as at Lancaster House in 1925 (the earlier IRC in England) but bad enough'. He got back to his Hotel at 12.15 am.

The next day was a Sunday and, despite his late night, Sir Henry was at the Cathedral for 8.00 am Communion. He then joined Sir Evelyn and Lady Cecil at the 10.00 am service at which he noted the large number of young men present in the congregation, which met with his wholehearted approval.

Lunch that Sunday was with the Egyptian Railways Assistant CME, a Mr Knight. In the afternoon, Knight took Henry and other guests for a run in the desert.

> The desert is sand and rock alright but not flat by any means. There were quite a lot of cars as it was Sunday or they do not allow single cars to go through. We had two. We came back to Cairo and a tea given by the Chief Traffic Manager. Tomorrow I should go to the Pyramids which should be a very interesting visit.

Monday morning was taken up with Congress meetings, at one of which Sir Henry and Nigel Gresley had a slight disagreement with the Chairman, but lost the argument. Most certainly the following afternoon produced its reporting material:

> Well, at all events I have ridden on a camel if I have not climbed a pyramid. Like many other things one reads and sees photos of them and then is just a little disappointed. I don't know why I should have been, for they are a very wonderful piece of work indeed and the mass effect is wonderful as is the view across Cairo, although when we got there, there was so much sand blowing that the view was not good but it improved later. Sir Evelyn and Lady Cecil both rode on camels and went much faster than mine did, but mine was young and I am heavy!

As the Congress continued, there was plenty to keep Sir Henry fully occupied in his General Secretary's rôle. However, some light relief came on the afternoon of Wednesday in the form of an excursion:

> We had a another wonderful visit yesterday to the pyramids and Tombs of Sakhara and Memphis. There is not a great deal at the latter place where there are two Colossi and one Sphinx. At the former there however is not only the stepped brick pyramid but a number of tombs three of which we went into. One has the 20 odd tombs of the Sacred Bulls which were buried in huge granite tombs which must weigh over 100 tons each. The other 2 tombs were wonderful with low bas-relief of ordinary Egyptian life 5000 years ago, some in colour.

The Thursday was busy, the morning at the Congress, with tea in the afternoon with the High Commissioner, Sir Percy Lovain, followed by a return to the Hotel for dinner before a late reception given by the Egyptian Prime Minister at the Semerarius Hotel. Henry commented later in his letter: 'I am hoping to have a quiet day tomorrow, only a lunch with the British Commercial Secretary in sight'. Clearly, the workload was beginning to tell on him, so much so that he was beginning to wonder if the planned trip to Palestine should be cancelled, but he knew he would never have another chance to come out.

Despite all his engagements Henry managed to attend some of the IRC meetings and find time to be vaccinated against smallpox. There was an outbreak in Ismailia and Port Said and, as he would be passing that way *en route* to Palestine, the precaution was obligatory.

Thursday, January 26th, that year was the end of Ramadan, when fasting between sunrise and sunset is required of a true Moslem. When the new moon appeared at 7.30 pm: 'The fast is broken and the three day feast of Bairam begins. The children were in very gay dress yesterday' he wrote on Saturday, 29th, continuing: 'and there were lots of carts going about crowded with women'. Henry had wished to photograph some of these festivities but had not the opportunity.

Now that the main bulk of the IRC business and meeting sessions were over, Sir Henry was able to take some walks around the city. Sunday the 29th found him at 7.30 Communion at the nearby Anglican church and then moving on to a Coptic church for the 10.00 am morning service:

There were two aisles and a nave, the north aisle being for women and separated by a curtain. I got the last seat in the nave. There was no choir in this church and the altar and apse were separated by a screen. The altar is a table and not against the wall and one could see was covered by an embroidered white cloth. On either side of the screen was a ready desk and a priest in black cloth with a hat like a Greek Orthodox priest read what were evidently the lessons. It looked strange him turning over what we think is the wrong way. There was chanting by boys and the congregation and a man who looked quite young gave a sermon for 20 minutes, The congregation, about 100 men all wore hats, mainly fez's [sic]. One in a kind of weird turban near me kept on murmuring and at one time turned to me and held out his hand. He did the same to others and just struck the palms together and did the same with me. Afterwards there was communion or Mass. A priest in the chancel in rich vestments some of which covered his head and went down his back, chanted in a weak voice and the congregation responded, bowed and crossed themselves. The priest finally uncovered the altar, ate bread and drank wine. Then a man in a white robe went round with a white sack of loaves which he gave to nearly everyone, receiving money (and giving change in some cases but not in mine). I hope to bring mine home. It is about 3 inches in diameter and has a pattern of crosses in the centre (I had a clean handkerchief and put it in it). Then the priest came through the screen and everyone crowded up to him (men only) and he broke pieces off other loaves and gave them to us. He did not hesitate to give me a piece. He had a very nice face. The Copts have remained Christian for over 1300 years often in the face of persecution. It was, to me, in the old church, very impressive.

Lunch after the Coptic church service was at a Major Beatty's, who was an old colleague of Henry's from his days at the RAF Farnborough, who now worked for the Shell oil company. Many a memory was aired of those hectic days during Sir Henry's Superintendency of that establishment, by this date the Royal Aircraft Establishment, and recognised as a world leader in aeronautical research.

In 1933, the Compounds were still doing good work on express duties, although production had been halted by Stanier. Here No. 1164, built by the Vulcan Foundry in 1925, heads a down express past Tring.   *R.S. Carpenter Collection*

In 1933 an example of the 'Royal Scot' class was sent to North America for an 11,000 mile tour of the USA and Canada. Although numbered as 6100, the locomotive was actually No. 6152 in disguise. On its return the bell and headlight were left in place for a short while. Here it is found in rather murky British weather at Preston.   *R.S. Carpenter Collection*

Chapter Thirteen

Palestine and the Return Home

The final sessions of the Congress wound up on 29th January and the delegates prepared to depart. Some of the British contingent were planning to stay on and see some more of Egypt and the Middle East, Sir Henry among them.

As he put it in the letter written that day: '31st January was my last day of real railway service'. The Congress was over and the previous day his last function as General Secretary had been to arrange a 'rather elaborate lunch' for the secretaries and translators who had done so much to assist in the smooth running of affairs.

Sir Henry had completed some 45 years of service on the railways, but his obvious sorrow that this was now over was tempered by the knowledge that soon he would be spending some weeks exploring the wonders of the Middle East on his long overland journey home to Emma.

To commence his journeying he was booked on a trip up the Nile, by train to Assouan (Aswan) and from there to Luxor. Aswan was, and still is, the farthest south one can travel on the railways in Egypt. He planned to return to Cairo on the following Sunday before setting off to Palestine. He had always wished to visit many of the places mentioned in his Bible Study classes and, like many Christians, a chance to achieve this was not to be missed. Nowadays this type of trip is fairly commonplace, but in the early 1930s such opportunities were rare.

The train for Aswan departed at 3.45 pm on its 500 mile journey, with one small delay when the locomotive developed a hot big end. The coaches comprised sleeping cars and dining saloons for this overnight journey down the western bank of the Nile. Henry penned a short letter to Emma *en route*, in which he commented further on his impressions of Cairo:

> I think it far and away the most wonderful city I have ever imagined. It, and not Bagdad, I can easily understand is the city of Arabian Nights as is I believe generally admitted. I could walk about the old streets for weeks and have put in all the time I could, finishing up today.

Upon a late arrival in the morning of 1st February, Sir Henry found Nigel Gresley, who was accompanied by Violet his daughter, had been established at the Cataract Hotel since the previous Thursday. Gresley appeared delighted to see Henry and the two of them took a sail in a felucca on the Nile that afternoon. Violet Gresley had contracted some sort of minor illness causing intermittent bouts of temperature, so her father had been rather at a loose end until the arrival of Fowler and his party.

Apart from some antiquities around here, the main attraction was the giant Aswan dam, then being increased in height by some 27 feet across its full width, which was over a mile: 'So that there will be much more water impounded by it. This is let out scientifically so that it may be used for irrigation right down through Egypt', wrote Henry from Aswan.

The final day of the stay at Aswan was taken up with a visit to a local village to see a demonstration of tribal sword dances and fights, followed by camel racing. After that was a visit to an alabaster quarry, finishing off with time in a bazaar, where Henry bought a few small items to take home for the family.

On early Friday morning, the 3rd February, Sir Henry left by train for Luxor. Gresley and his daughter having made the same journey the previous day.

Once settled in at the Luxor Hotel, a further letter was started:

> This is I think the nicest hotel I have been in. It is not too big and is in a garden away from the road. There are more flowers here than I have seen in a garden . . . I have at all events started on my way back to you, if it is to be a wandering one. There are a lot of water wagtails everywhere we go. I have seen a few hoopoes which are a black and white bird with the crown King Solomon gave it but I cannot think, neither can anyone I have spoken to, why he gave it to them. What was delightful at Assouan was to see a few swallows and to think that they might have been at Spondon.

Saturday 4th February found Henry being conducted around the nearby temples and tombs for some four hours. His comments on what he saw are illuminating: '. . . if anyone said that Thebes had 1,000 gates instead of 100 I should agree. What a mass of wonderful things to be sure'. This was to be his final day of sightseeing in Egypt and the following day he was disappointed at not being able to attend church, which he had faithfully done up to now. The train for Cairo left Luxor at 6.45 am, taking some 12 hours leisurely progress to the capital. Henry had some comments to make regarding Egypt as a whole:

> They say that this is the land of flies and dust. There are a few of the former which sometimes are very insistent, but there is no doubt about the latter. It gets in everywhere and covers every thing. I don't know what you would say about the carriage. [He also described his feelings on the previous day's trip to the tombs in the Valley of the Kings.] One, of course, was Tutankhamen's; it was small and simple and yet contained all that wonderful mass of treasure which is in the Museum at Cairo. The other one was that of Seti I which was despoiled years and years ago. This seemed to be 10 times the size and if as richly furnished the things taken out must have been tremendous. The Valley of the Kings itself is a stoney desolate place right away in those sandstone hills.

Although they had expected the train to be running late, it actually arrived in Cairo on time. Sir Henry made for the Victoria Hotel for a busy and late evening preparing his trunk for despatch home, as he intended to travel home through Palestine with the minimum of luggage. The following morning he was informed that, for his rail journey to and through Palestine, the General Manager of the Palestine Railways, a Mr Webb, had arranged for him to have the use of the Palestine sleeping saloon from the East bank of the Suez canal. 'I don't know what they would do if a really high class railway man came!', he reported to Emma.

Gresley was back in Cairo and on Monday morning, the 6th February, had visited the Egyptian Railways' new workshops in the capacity of Consulting Engineer. Sir Henry had spent the morning at the Railway Offices and found that he had just enough time that afternoon to arrange a visit to these facilities, before making for the station to pick up his train at 6.00 pm for Ismailia, where he was to cross the Suez Canal.

Several other Congress attendees were on the train, some of whom were returning home by boat. The general opinion was that it had been a good Congress technically and, as Henry wrote to Emma: 'There is no doubt of it being a good one from the enjoyment stand-point'.

His first destination was to be Gaza, where he was to visit an established archaeological excavation run by Sir Flinders Petrie. He had been invited to go and stay there some time ago, so this seemed an ideal opportunity to accept the invitation.

Within four hours of leaving Cairo, he was sitting in the private saloon, having crossed the canal by launch. His letter of the 6th February describes his feelings on this honour: 'I am wondering if I can live up to this for I have a saloon with three beds and apparantly it is at my disposal whilst I am in Palestine, although I only want it to Gaza'.

The overnight journey to Gaza passed quietly and restfully, the saloon being uncoupled and shunted into a siding at Gaza station at about 5.00 am. Following a leisurely breakfast, prepared and served by 'George' ('I believe they are all that name'), the servant that came with the saloon, Henry penned a few extra lines to his letter of that day before getting off and walking the mile from the station into the town of Gaza. It had been raining heavily earlier, and more looked possible at any moment, which had created quite a pleasant fresh air and also, to his intense pleasure, laid the dust.

Gaza he found very interesting:

I first went down a street in which nearly every little shop had two hand looms in which two men were making carpets or cloth. I then went to the Post Office, which flew a Union Jack upside down, as a result of this I went across to the Police Station to tell them about it. Here I met a smart English Lieutenant of Police and had a talk with him. I went to look at one mosque and another where afterwards found that they wanted 10s. to let a Christian in. More bazaars, partially covered in, selling all sorts of things (and apparently without trade as so many are).

Sir Henry then arrived at the garage with which it had been arranged for him to obtain transport to the site he was to visit.

The rain had now recommenced and the five mile drive to the camp site was not without problems, as towards the end the driver managed to veer off the road and get the vehicle stuck in the mud up to àxle depth. However, 'Out we hopped and soon a lot of men came running up and we pushed and the engine did its best and out we pushed her, being watched with field glasses from the camp as I afterwards found'. Following this slight delay, he arrived at the archaeological camp at Tel el Azzul, which consisted of a number of low mud brick buildings with corrugated iron roofs. Sir Flinders and Lady Petrie, with their daughter, were there to greet him and made him as comfortable as could be in the rather basic surroundings.

His first afternoon was spent visiting the native workers' tented camp with a Mr Falconer, one of Sir Flinders' chief assistants. They were invited into one of the tents: 'just like the one at the CMS* exhibition, but larger', wrote Henry. Falconer spoke fluent Arabic and was able to translate for him in the conversation that ensued. After supper at 6.45 pm five of the people on the site, including Sir Henry, retired to the 'reading room' which was used for social occasions and as a study for writing up the archaeological records.

* Church Missionary Society

Next morning, 8th February, the overnight rain continued pouring down until about 9.30 am. The digging could not start due to this and the nearby wadi (valley) was by now in flood. Once the rain had ceased, Henry ventured out to investigate the excavations, which were uncovering the remains of some palaces which had mud walls just like the ones employed for the temporary accommodation for the staff. He found the work being carried out fascinating, likewise the people involved:

> There are I believe about 200 folks altogether and most of them are children. They carry the sand on their heads in baskets about 13 inches in diameter and 5 inches deep. the girls (also women in Gaza) have coins sewn onto their headdress, some quite a lot and big ones too. It represents their dowry, I believe. They are paid for anything they find worth keeping. A little while ago a man was paid £40 for some gold object and he at once bought a wife and a donkey!

He then spent most of the day investigating the five main places where digging was taking place, in the company of Sir Flinders Petrie who was 'a splendid talker, as I know he is a lecturer, and I have tried to be a good listener'.

The next day, the weather had improved. The sun shone from a cloudless sky and that afternoon a Dr Hargreaves from the CMS Medical Mission Hospital in Gaza visited the camp together with his wife and a Mr and Mrs Coates from Birmingham. Henry had for a long time been interested in the work of the CMS and, feeling that by this time he had stayed long enough with the Petries at the camp, talked this over with Dr Hargreaves. It was arranged that he should go and stay with the Doctor in Gaza until the following Monday, when he was due to go to Jerusalem. Whilst in Gaza he was just a few miles from the site of Ascalon, where Sir Richard Fowler received his knighthood, as recounted in Chapter Four. He was to find waiting for him on his return from this trip, a book concerning an account of the Fowler family which contained a paragraph describing that knighthood. Probably, had he known of this fact when at Gaza, he would have made the short trip of some 11 miles to view the place which brought that first honour to his family.

The following Monday morning found him bidding farewell to the Hargreaves at Gaza station and reboarding the Palestine saloon to continue his journey to Jerusalem, where he was to stay a few days. In fact, Sir Henry would have passed through Ashqelon (Ascalon), the first station along the line, on his journey from Gaza to Jerusalem.

From Monday 14th to Thursday 17th February, Sir Henry spent four glorious days investigating and sampling the sights of that ancient city. His letter from here has not survived so we are in the dark as to his explorations here. But doubtless he would have visited the site of the Temple, trudged down part of the Via d'Elrosa and gone to the supposed sites of the Crucifixion and Tomb in addition to viewing the walls of the old city: 'One was quite glad that the walls of Jerusalem at present keep the old town intact and confined, even if it does smell!', he wrote in his letter from Tiberias. However, it is obvious that during his time in Jerusalem he rearranged his schedule by cutting out the onward rail journey to Tiberias, and instead planning to accomplish that part of his journeying by bus.

The morning of the 17th found him on board a bus passing through:

> . . . the centre of Palestine (cost rather under 5 shillings, including luggage). We went, amongst other places, through Sychem, between Mounts Ebal and Gerizim and saw Jacob's Well, quite close to Samaria. The Mountains of Gilboa where Saul and Jonathan were killed lay to the left. At one point we got a good view which on a clear day would have been marvellous,as you could have seen most of the North and centre of Palestine. As it was it was fine with the sea away to the West and the snow clad top of Hermon to the North. Later we went across the plain of Esdraelon and Mount Tabor was on the right. Many of the battles of ancient history were fought here.

His Bible studies were coming alive as he passed near or through so many places that featured in his readings and teachings back home. One such place was Nazareth, where the state of the approach roads produced some comments: 'There were before this enough hairpin bends on the mountains to last us a long while. The worst, however, were those on the hill or mountain leading to Nazareth. It is quite a town with some big buildings, evidently religious houses.'

His journey continued until at 3.00 pm he arrived in Tiberias and settled into the Hotel Tiberias. This establishment still exists today, having been much rebuilt and improved over the years and is still used by many who tour Israel. He then proceeded to plan an excursion to Capurnaum the following day, after first taking a walk around the walled city with its castle dating back to the Crusades. He went on to note his findings to Emma that night: 'There is a Scottish Mission Hospital right against it (the castle) now. The Sea of Galilee is indeed surrounded by mountains with Hermon (over 9,000 feet high) at the end. It has a fairly flat top and is not the cone I imagined. The streets except 2 or 3, are narrow with the drain down the centre'.

As always, he was on the lookout for unusual plants. His habit was, where possible, to take cuttings or roots home from abroad, but due to the length of time before he was to return home did not hold out much hope of getting much back on this trip, apart from from some roots of a black iris posted on to him in Jerusalem by the Hargreaves in Gaza.

The next morning at 8.30 he was in a hired car *en route* to Capurnaum, of the faithful Centurion fame, where he explored the ruins of the Roman town and its synagogue to reawaken the memories of a famous Bible account of Jesus' ministry there.

There was just time to take a further quick look through Tiberias and indulge in a bath at the recently restored hot sulphur springs, before going to the station to catch the 1.00 pm train for Damascus, his next scheduled stop on this overland return to England.

The railway involved for this seven-hour journey was the Hedjaz Railway which Henry found somewhat lacking; 'although 1st class, is nothing great'. He had some comments to make on the rough riding, which may well have been accentuated by the narrow track gauge of 3 ft 5 in. - the only recorded use of this non-standard dimension, which some reports claimed to be caused by the result of incorrect drilling of the holes in the metal sleepers employed - but probably due to the destructive effect of the war which had raged along that line as

Lawrence forced the Turks back from their invasion of Palestine. He arrived in Damascus a bit behind time and repaired to the Hotel Omarjad where he found two letters from Emma and one from Dorothea awaiting him, which he read with great interest. He had been away now for some seven weeks and clearly missed the companionship of Emma as well as being concerned for her condition.

Rising early on Sunday morning, Sir Henry penned a few lines to Emma before breakfast:

> It rained in the night and still looks a little watery but is dry at present. Doubtless you know that Tiberias is the chief seat of the Sultan of Baraghit (the King of the Fleas). I thought I had escaped the attention of his highness, but one of the very small and unimportant of his subjects evidently followed me. I think most likely in that train.

He was to stay in Damascus for three days, exploring the city and probably comparing it, as much as he could, with the place it was when Saul was led there, blinded, from his experience on the road to Damascus. He was indeed treading on historic ground.

His time in Damascus at an end, he boarded the train for the journey to Constantinople (Istanbul), which took some 10 hours, arriving on the 25th February. The hotel selected for the brief stay here was the Pera Palace. The following morning, after receiving another letter from Emma, he sat down to write a brief note to her, describing an incident which he had witnessed in the city earlier. He had called at Cook's office near the Hotel, after which he took a walk round the city to explore it, during which he located the English Church and noted the times for the following day's services. He had then decided to find a real Turkish Bath and, spotting another Cook's office near the Galata Bridge, went in to ask about the whereabouts of a suitable one. Cook's

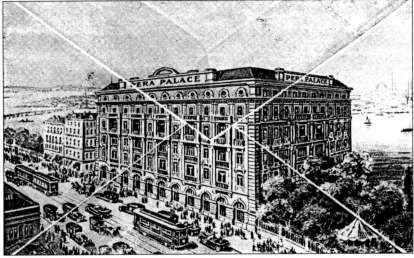

The Pera Palace Hotel, Istanbul, where Sir Henry stayed on his journey home. Taken from the back of an envelope of a letter sent from that city.   *Mrs D. Fowler*

recommended a good bath, which he visited, and then caught a tram back to the Hotel. As the tram passed the Cook's office near the Galata Bridge a group of young men were seen to throw missiles at it, doing considerable damage. The sight of this enraged Sir Henry: 'I felt like getting out and butting in but remembered what it says about 'discretion' and 'valour'. A fellow who spoke French in the tram said there has been some trouble about a new manager (who I have not met)'. Sir Henry could speak reasonable French, much of it picked up during his frequent visits during the latter war years and also on the several cycling holidays taken there. This linguistic ability, on occasions, proved useful during IRC sessions as well as when travelling in the company of foreigners who had French as an extra language.

The next day, it being Sunday, Sir Henry attended the 8.00 am service at the Crimea Church, being invited into the Chaplain's house for tea and toast afterwards by the vicar, a Father Pollard. The weather that day was very overcast and wet: 'But I have still a mackintosh and the "remains" of my most faithful companion on my trip, "my umberella" [sic].'

The next morning, 27th February, Sir Henry left Istanbul for Venice, where he stopped one night before continuing his rail journey to the Channel port and the sea crossing to England. He was reunited with Emma on Friday 3rd March and settled back into a busy retirement, happy to be at home for a brief spell and have his family around him. He had been abroad for almost nine weeks.

'Royal Scot' No. 6104 *Scottish Borderer* passing Tring on up express in 1933.

R.S. Carpenter Collection

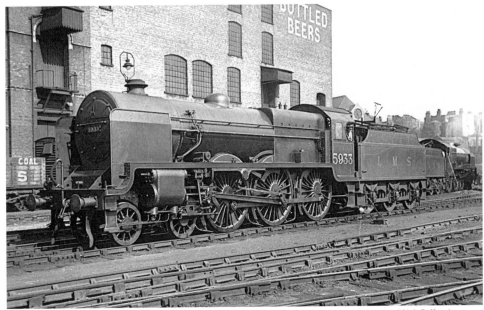

'Patriot' No. 5933 at Kentish Town 1933.   *JSM Collection*

The Deeley 0-6-4T still in service in 1935, seen here with a 'merry-go-round' coal train. Note the
rather modern looking bogie hopper wagons.   *JSM Collection*

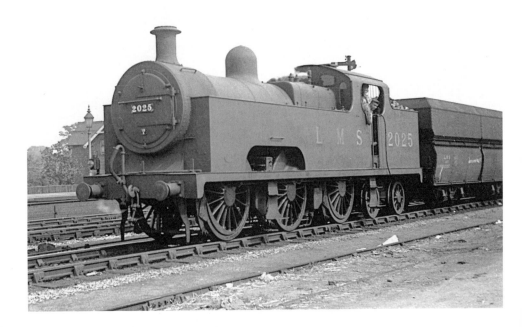

Chapter Fourteen

The Final Years

Within five days of his return from Egypt and Palestine, Sir Henry was due to attend the Institute of Metals dinner in London to give an address he had prepared over the weeks of his travels. Emma came to London with him and they stayed, as usual, at the St Pancras Hotel. She had to return on an early train the following morning in order to attend her usual Thursday court hearing.

Easter 1933, saw Harry and his family coming to stay at Spondon Hall. His wife, Edith, was taken ill on the Good Friday and immediately dispatched to a Nursing Home in Derby. Daughter Jenifer, now three, stayed with her grandmother and was proudly taken round to friends' houses for tea whilst her mother recovered. After treatment, Edith went back to Spondon Hall for convalescence before Harry returned and took them home on the 14th May.

The end of June that year was a hot time, and on the 22nd Sir Henry spent the early part of the day at the National Physical Laboratory, followed by a management research meeting in London. His commitments were now much reduced and he often could be found relaxing at the Athenaeum Club in Pall Mall, enjoying a pot of tea and a muffin, after his meetings.

He was now beginning to find some free time, and spent a few days at Derby County Cricket Club grounds, a short drive along the Nottingham Road into Derby. On occasions, Lady Emma would accompany him if her diary permitted, and they would pass the time quietly relaxing and watching the game unfold.

That autumn, Henry made a short visit to France. The crossing was quite rough, with the boat rolling considerably, But Henry was not to be stricken with sea-sickness this time: 'I stood up on deck for some time until the water began to fly over. I fancy that it got a little smoother as we got across but I rather enjoyed it'. *En route* from Calais to Paris he met the ex-CME of the Metropolitan Railway who had been instrumental in the building of six 2-6-4Ts using surplus parts bought from the Woolwich Arsenal batch of 100 Maunsell 'N' class 2-6-0s. This person, a Mr Halley, was currently the Operating Manager of the London Transport Board railway system.

On 22nd November Henry was in London again for some more meetings. This time he stayed at the Royal Automobile Club, taking advantage of their pool to get a swim in the morning. He was a bit concerned about his weight and tried to get some exercise to trim some off whenever possible. Emma was not on top form, having missed two weeks of her Court attendances through illness, and he made a point of writing to her even though he was only away a couple of nights. She did, however, recover sufficiently to be able to attend the Women's Institute party on the 23rd, and also to fulfill a piano playing engagement at a Dr Barnardo's event on the 24th. Emma's musical talents had been handed down to Dorothea who, it is said by the family, could have become a concert pianist such was her ability.

Back on the LMS, Stanier had begun to take stock of the situation and, although Anderson had put in requests for so many locomotives of a specific (existing) type, took no action, just putting the relevant memos in his Pending tray. When Anderson asked why he had not replied, he was told that a reply would not be forthcoming, as: 'I am trying to decide what range of new locomotives you need, and I can only do this if you will specify the numbers required and the duties they are to perform'. Anderson got the message and soon the LDO was busy preparing diagrams of Stanier's proposed types.

Much of what had been accepted as normal Derby practice was swept away to be replaced by Swindon precepts. Chambers, still chief draughtsman at Derby had some difficulty in accepting some of these, he was too steeped in Derby tradition. He was, therefore, 'promoted' to the post of Technical Assistant at Euston, being replaced by Tom Coleman from Horwich. Coleman was fully in accord with many of Stanier's proposals and not likely to query new practices. He also imported the graceful artistic appearances of Horwich designs and incorporated them on Stanier's products. One only has to compare the Horwich design studies with the range of standard types produced for the LMS from 1933 onwards to see this.

In 1933 came the first new locomotives, fifteen 2-6-0s and the first two Pacifics. The latter bore a strong resemblance to the abortive compound design promoted by Sir Henry some eight years previously. The small engine policy was never to return. Over the following six years Stanier re-stocked the LMS with over 1,200 new engines, all six- or eight-coupled, whilst keeping the best of Fowler's and progressively scrapping many of the obsolete types with their antiquated technology. The story of how that was achieved is another matter, outside this narrative, save that the mainstay of the express fleet whilst this was going on, were the Fowler 'Royal Scot' and 'Patriot' classes. Sir Henry had most certainly seen to it that this important feature was catered for. Also Stanier kept the '4F' 0-6-0 in production, there being no better mid-range all-rounder available. The cost of designing a replacement could not compete with the continued production of a standard type of which there were over 700 in service.

In 1934, after Eric had accumulated some police experience in Derby he had been admitted to Grays Inn, intending to complete his studies for the Bar. Up to his call to the Bar, he continued his police career. Emma was by now quite seriously ill and confined to home towards the end of the year. Tragically, on the 1st November, her birthday, she died. She was 63, and greatly missed by the family and all her many friends in the town which had been their home for 34 years.

Just prior to his loss, in September, Sir Henry had been attending a conference of the British Association at Aberdeen, still throwing himself wholeheartedly into forums and discussions as speaker and chairman. He still obviously looked upon himself as fully able, despite advancing years, to apply his expertise on many engineering and other matters. However, during the conference, he became suddenly unwell, and the doctor who examined him was extremely concerned and prescribed an immediate return home and complete rest. Sir Josiah Stamp was attending the conference, and once he heard of Fowler's plight, immediately took matters into his hands. Arrangements were made for Sir Henry to travel by express to Crewe, accompanied by a nurse, where a special train awaited his arrival to transport him to Derby. This special train was met at Derby by one of the LMS ambulances to transfer him home to Spondon Hall. His own doctor confirmed the need for rest and all his engagements for the following several weeks were cancelled. The warning was there for Henry, to start reducing the workload. His full life was now beginning to take its toll of his robust physique, but this reduction was not in his nature, and the adjustment was fitful.

Faithful Dorothea stayed at hand with her grieving father after the funeral of Emma, which Henry did not attend, his health having been dealt a shattering blow with this loss. It was some considerable time before he was able to get back into some semblance of his old self, but he was never the same man again. He and Emma had been very close, one only needs to read some of his letters to see how much he doted on her, and her passing created a void in the remainder of his life. Her death on her birthday, a day on which he always placed a great emphasis, was particularly poignant, for it was 42 years ago, at her 21st, that he had decided that here was the woman for him.

However, there was a bright turn of events at the end of 1934, when Eric Fowler became engaged to Gwendoline May Bignell from Nuthall, Nottinghamshire. Gwen (Bennie to her family and friends) had been around for some time now, and had spent the 1933 Christmas at Spondon Hall. Sir Henry was by this time recovering his health and looked forward to the forthcoming wedding.

The family rallied round their still grieving father and tactfully suggested that his Christmas that year might be spent away from the memories at Spondon. Sir Henry took their advice and in late November was to be found aboard the P&O SS *Malaya, en route* for Australia. At least on board ship he was away from the stresses of work and could accommodate better his great loss. The month's voyage to Sydney took in Marseilles, Port Said, Aden, Bombay, Colombo and Freemantle. The initial journey, as far as Port Said, must have brought back memories of that two years previously going out to the Cairo conference. This time he saw the Suez Canal from a different angle: 'At Port Said we entered the Suez Canal and went slowly about 7 miles per hour. It got dark when we were about half way through. When I wakened in the morning there were mountains on the shore on either side and the sea was very blue. We were in the Gulf of Suez . . .' On 2nd December they called at Aden where, after attending the morning service on board, he went ashore for a few hours and: '. . . was really surprised at the number of camels which were in use. Nothing but camels and motor cars'. By late afternoon they were *en route* for Bombay, where the letter containing the above statements was air-mailed to Spondon.

Christmas was spent in Sydney, where Sir Henry soon became known to the Bishop of Sydney after attending service at the cathedral there, spending the evening back at Bishopscourt the Bishop's official residence, being entertained for supper.

A couple of weeks were spent in Australia before setting sail again, for New Zealand. His travels there are unknown save for being at Rotorua on 15th January, 1935, a postcard written there being the only surviving communication. The journey home was uneventful and he arrived back much refreshed, ready to get back to some of his outside interests.

Sir Henry's Bible class reunion 1935, outside the Iron Hut. Many of the elder members in this photograph were those supported during the War.   *Miss J. Wright*

Spondon Old Folks Tea to commemorate the Silver Jubilee in 1935. Sir Henry at rear.
                                                                                    Miss J. Wright

During 1935, he returned to his chairmanship duties for the Noise Prevention Committee of the Ministry of Transport, but the old vigour had gone and he must have been glad of the opportunity to relax more often than in his full days during his railway service. Supported by Dorothea, he continued to live at Spondon Hall in between his trips covering the deliberations of the Ministry committee. His personality certainly had recovered somewhat, as when Eric announced the date of his wedding, Henry insisted on organising this on a grand scale, with the service at Spondon Parish Church and the reception that followed in a marquee in the grounds of Spondon Hall. This event took place on 16th April, 1936, although by this time Sir Henry's health was giving cause for concern.

Eric later, in 1937, was called to the Bar, and practised as a barrister up to the outbreak of war in 1939. His time of fame was to come when, as a navigator in Bomber Command, he was awarded the DFC for exploits over Germany in 1941. Sir Henry, had he still been alive, would have been justly proud of his airman son. Whether his own experiences in the aviation sphere during World War I ever had any influence on Eric's choice of fighting arm is not clear, but seems possible.

Sir Henry Fowler's health grew worse as 1937 passed and while he was still able to participate in some of his outside interests, the zest for life was now slipping away. He stubbornly kept going in the face of increasing health problems, the illness being really a series of mini-strokes which began to incapacitate him considerably, as they affected his movements. It must have been very frustrating for him, such an active person, to be increasingly restricted by this. A nurse was now in residence at Spondon Hall to cater for his needs, and frequently he was to be found in a wheelchair. The strokes were becoming progressively worse and his Ministry responsibilities had now ceased. One of his great hobbies, that of bell-ringing was now out of the question and he handed over his Captainship to one of his long-time companions in the belfry, George Wright. On 8th January, 1938, he wrote:

Dear George,
   I was very delighted to hear that you are going to look after the bell ringing. As you know I want to help all I can and hope I shall soon be able to do something.
      Yours sincerely
      Hy Fowler

Shortly after this, he suffered yet another stroke, yet with determination, made a partial recovery sufficient to pen a short note to Cecelia and Joyce Wright for their assistance in finding 'Bun' pennies for a collection for the Infirmary he had organised at the Church.

Dear Cecilia and Joyce.
   Thank you so much for the 'Bun' pennies you so kindly sent me. I have put them with the bag I have and send in on Nov 1st, the anniversary of Lady Fowler's death and have added the money to the egg money I send to the Infirmary.
      Thank you so much,
      Yours Hy Fowler

The Fowler grave in Nottingham Road Cemetery, Derby.   *(All) Author*

The writing in this letter, although recogniseable, was most certainly shaky and pointed to a worsening of Sir Henry's condition, although, even in the final days his sense of humour still stayed with him, for some little time later, Eric Fowler appeared at the Wright's door bearing a big 'bunch of camelias for Cecilia' to cheer up Mrs Wright up after a bout of illness. Had he been fitter, Sir Henry himself would have made the presentation.

The end came with a sudden worsening of his condition just a few days before his death, on the 16th October, which was a Sunday. The following Wednesday, a funeral service was held at Spondon Parish Church, which was kept as simple as possible, with no flowers by request. The clergy present consisted of the vicar and curate of Spondon, the Revds H.C. Brocklehurst and C. Herve, assisted by the Revd J.E. Dallimore, a life-long friend of Sir Henry. The cortege carried in the coffin of English oak, which bore the simple inscription: 'Henry Fowler, at rest, 16 October 1938, aged 68'.

Practically every top position and department on the LMS was represented, either by the head or a delegated assistant. Oliver Bulleid was present to represent the ARLE, James Clayton returned to Derby on behalf of the Southern Railway in the company of G.S. Szlumper, the new General Manager. The I.Mech.E., I.Civil E. and I.Auto.E. were present, as were many of the Universities and Colleges Sir Henry had connections with. On the sporting side both hockey and cricket representatives were prominent as were the many Church bodies whom he had served on.

The list of attendees is impressive and shows the esteem that Sir Henry was held in by them. Many inhabitants of Spondon, who had known the Fowlers paid their last respects to him at the service.

Spondon Hall, sadly neglected and shortly to be demolished, 11th October, 1949.
Derby Telegraph

The cricket club pavilion today at Spondon   *Author*

The memorial gates to Lady Fowler at St Werburgh's Church.   *Author*

Derby Railway Works, 1999. In the distance are the old erection shops, soon to be hidden from view by the new structure seen going up on what was the site of roundhouses 2 and 3.

Author

To that end the obituary published in the St Werburgh's Parish magazine is printed in full as an appendix to this book. This gives a splendid picture of Sir Henry's life around that church.

Harry, Dorothea and Eric, plus their uncles Alec and Charles were the principal family mourners who, after the service, travelled to the graveside to see his coffin laid to rest in the family grave beside his beloved Emma and seven month old baby Geoffrey whose short life had ended 35 years previously. A great organiser, famous engineer, a devoted family man and a sincere Christian had gone. Spondon Hall never again resounded to the bustle of a busy life, and lay empty until sold to Derby Children's Hospital for conversion to an annex. This was never carried out, as the onset of World War II found it requisitioned for use as an officer training centre. After the war it fell into disuse, as plans for a new bypass meant that a major road would pass close by and so, in 1958, the by now very dilapidated building was pulled down. The land was sold off and allocated for building, with the many exotic trees and shrubs imported and nurtured over the years by Sir Henry uprooted and destroyed. A housing estate now covers what used to be the grounds of the Hall, with one avenue named after Sir Henry Fowler, a tangible memorial to a well-loved former inhabitant, who had achieved so much for his Country and employers in a rich and versatile life.

Fowler Avenue, Spondon. This estate was built on what used to be the grounds of Spondon Hall.

Author

Appendix One

Sir Henry Fowler
Obituary

1. St Werburgh's Church, Spondon

In the passing away of Sir Henry Fowler, we have suffered a great loss. In his busy life, brim full of all sorts of activities and responsibilities, his work for the Church was always looked upon as of the utmost importance. For many years he had been an outstanding figure in the Engineering world, and at the same time played a very important part, not only in this Parish, which he loved so dearly, but also in the Diocese. We shall miss him very greatly.

In thinking over his life among us here certain things seem especially to associate themselves with him in my mind. He was a generous supporter of the Mission as it was run in the old days with a Church Army Captain. Though it was a disappointment when it became obvious, through the rapid growth in population, that the C.A. Captain would have to give way to an assistant Priest, he made it clear that he was ready to support me. I well remember his words at the end of an interview I had with him in connection with this matter; how he took my hand and said, 'Well, Vicar, you know I cannot see eye to eye with you in everything, but I must remember that the responsibility is yours and not mine, and no doubt you are doing right'.

Among his many activities he was a very keen Bell-ringer. Unless some urgent cause called him elsewhere he was always to be found in the Belfry, on Sunday mornings, lending a hand with one of the bells. It was sad when failing health deprived him of this self-imposed task.

He also took special interest in the Churchyard. Coming from a part of the country where they take great pride in their Churchyards it was a great satisfaction when, after the expenditure of much labour, it was, at last, possible to mow the grass and keep it neat and tidy - a marked improvement to the tousled appearance it used to have some 12 years ago. Also in connection with the Churchyard, about four years ago, he gave the pair of new gates by the North door of the Church, in memory of Lady Fowler. He made a special request that no public acknowledgment should be made of this at the time. But now he is no longer with us, I think it is only right that people should know of this benefaction.

But where his influence was felt most was amongst the young men who attended his Bible Class, on Sunday afternoons. Young men had a very warm place in his heart, and he was always anxious to do all that he could for them. The Class was a great joy to him, and I am sure it was also to those who listened to his teaching. It was a sad time when he could no longer carry on with it.

Many will remember, with gratitude, the visits to London and abroad he organised for them. A still larger number will cherish the memory of the Social evenings, for past and present members, which he and Lady Fowler used to arrange in the Mission Hall, at Christmastime - the whist, the refreshments, the goodly hamper of pears which always seemed to be available, the community singing which always included the old song about 'Solomon Levi' and brought back memories of riotous times. And not least, the smoke! Though Sir Henry was a non-smoker himself the atmosphere towards the end of the evening was thick enough for the most hardened smoker! Indeed we shall miss him greatly. He was a true Servant of God, and his influence among us will last on us for many a long day.

Revd H.C. Brocklehurst
St Werburgh's Church
Spondon
November 1938

2. The International Railway Congress Association

We deeply regret to record the death of Sir Henry Fowler, KBE, formerly Chief Mechanical Engineer, later Assistant to Vice-President for Research and Development, London Midland and Scottish Railway.

Sir Henry was born on July 29th, 1870, and educated at Evesham and at the Mason Science College, Birmingham, and was apprenticed at the Horwich Works of the lancashire and Yorkshire Railway, being subsequently appointed Assistant, then Chief of the Testing Department, and finally Gas Engineer of the company. Whilst at Horwich, he was closely associated with the work of the Railway Mechanic's Institute, first as a student, and then as a teacher.

In 1900, Sir Henry left the Lancashire and Yorkshire Railway to take up the position of Gas Engineer on the Midland Railway; in 1905, he became Works Assistant and in 1907, Works Manager, Derby. In 1909, he was appointed Chief Mechanical Engineer of the Midland Railway, which position he held until the formation of the London Midland and Scottish Railway in 1923, when he was made Deputy Chief Mechanical Engineer for the whole undertaking, as well as Mechanical Engineer for the Midland Division. In 1925, following the retirement of Mr George Hughes, his former chief at Horwich, he was appointed Chief Mechanical Engineer, London Midland and Scottish Railway, which position he held until the end of 1930, when he became Assistant to the Vice-President for Works (Research and Development). He retired from this position in 1933, being elected the next year by the Ministry of Transport as Chairman of a committee appointed to investigate the noise in connection with mechanically propelled vehicles.

In 1907, Sir Henry had visited America, where he gained much experience in railway and mechanical matters.

During the War, he was appointed Director of Production, Ministry of Munitions, in 1915, Superintendent of the Royal Aircraft Factory in 1916, Assistant Director General of Aircraft Production in 1917, and subsequently held various other positions under the Ministry from 1918 to 1919.

He was created CBE in 1917, and KBE in 1918, for his services in this latter connection.

Sir Henry was a full member of the Institution of Civil Engineers and a member of Council of the Institution. Papers read before the Institution gained him the Miller Prize, the Telford Premium, the Watt Medal and the Webb Prize.

In 1922, he collaborated with Sir Nigel Gresley (then Mr) in presenting to that Institution a paper on the results of brake trials with long goods trains.

He was President of the Institutions of Mechanical Engineers (1927), Locomotive Engineers (1912-14), Automobile Engineers (1920-21), of the University of Birmingham Engineering Society (1912-14), of the Engineering Section of the British Association for the Advancement of Science (1923), and the Institute of Metals (1932). He was also a member of the Institute of Transport, and was awarded the Railway Engineering Gold Medal by the Council of that Institute (1929-30). He held the honorary degree of LL D from the University of Birmingham, and of DSc from the University of Manchester, and he was the first honorary graduate of the Manchester College of Technology.

Sir Henry had been a member of the Permanent Commission of the International Railway Congress Association since 1925, and took a very active part in the London (1925), Madrid (1930), and Cairo (1933) Sessions, being in each case appointed assistant General Secretary, and presenting reports on the following subjects:

In 1930 - Question VI: Investigation into the static and dynamic stresses in railway bridges (in collaboration with Mr G. Ellson).

In 1933 - Question III: Methods to be used to increase the mileage run by locomotives between two repairs including lifting. Sir Henry also drew up the special report summing up the three reports presented by this Question.

Already in 1922, at the Rome Session, he read a very interesting note on the utility of studying the question of the use of liquid fuel in locomotives.

In collaboration with Mr Barriol, General Secretary of the Paris Statistics Department, Sir Henry audited the accountancy of the Association for the periods ending with the London (1925), Madrid (1930) and Cairo (1933) Sessions.

Thanks to his ceaseless activity and cheerful disposition, Sir Henry was held in very high esteem by his colleagues of the Permanent Commission, who will keep the best of remembrances of him.

We wish to convey our sincerest sympathy to his family.

The Executive Committee

Sir Henry Fowler, KBE.
© *(British) Crown Copyright, 1999 Defence Evaluation and Research Agency, reproduced with the permission of the Controller, Her (Britannic) Majesty's Stationary Office*

Locomotive Production Rates
1923-1931

LMS Works	1923	1924	1925	1926	1927	1928	1929	1930	1931
Derby		ac	ac	a	ah	hij	hij	gilm	il
Crewe		a	a	ae	ae	ae	ek	ek	ek
St Rollox		a		a	a	a			
Horwich			c	ce	e	a	e	de	
Private Builders									
North British		d	aj	ad	adg				
Kerr Stuart			a	a	a				
Barclay				a	a				
Stephenson			b						
Vulcan Foundry		d	c	d	cd	d			
Hunslet		d	d	d	d	d			
Bagnall				d	d	d			
Beardmore						d	d		
Beyer, Peacock					f			f	
No. Produced	-	142	191	303	373	330	225	157	111

A grand total of 1,832 locomotives over eight years, not including extra types for the NCC arm of the LMS.

Key

a	'4F' class 0-6-0	f	'Garratt' 2-6-0+0-6-2	k	'7F' class 0-8-0
b	'7F' class 2-8-0	g	'6P' 'Royal Scot' class 4-6-0	l	'3P' class 2-6-2T
c	'4P' class 4-4-0	h	'4P' class 2-6-4T	m	'5XP' 'Patriot' class 4-6-0
d	'3F' class 0-6-0T	i	'2P' class 4-4-0		
e	'5P4F' class 2-6-0	j	'2F' class 0-6-0T		

'Royal Scot' class 4-6-0 No. 6155 *The Lancer* is seen approaching Saltney Jn, north of Chester with a North Wales express in the 1930s. *A.W.V. Mace Collection*

Appendix Three

Summary of Fowler Locomotives Built between 1911 and 1941

Class	Type	First Batch	Sub Batches	Number Built	
'4F'	0-6-0	1911	1917-41	772	*
'7F'	2-8-0	1914	1925	11	
-	0-10-0	1919	-	1	
'4P'	4-4-0	1924	1925-32	195	#
'3F'	0-6-0T	1924	1925-30	422	*
'5P5F'	2-6-0	1926	1927-32	245	*
Garrett	2-6-0+0-6-2	1927	1930	33	
'6P'	4-6-0	1927	1930	70	
'4P'	2-6-4T	1927	1928-34	125	*
'2P'	4-4-0	1928	1929-32	138	
'2F'	0-6-0T	1928	1929	10	*
'7F'	0-8-0	1929	1930-32	175	
'3P'	2-6-2T	1930	1930-32	70	
'6P'	4-6-0	1930	-	1	†
'6P'	4-6-0	1930	1932-34	52	

Grand Total   2,320

Notes: *   A 'standard' LMS class
        †   Experimental high pressure locomotive
        #   Compound

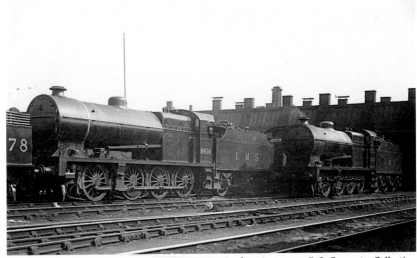

Two 0-8-0s at Crewe South. Nos. 9615/6 await further duties.   *R.S. Carpenter Collection*

Appendix Four

Supplementary locomotives built during Fowler's time as CME

Type	When built	Subsequent batches	Number
4-4-0	1914	1922	4 *
4-4-2T	1923	1928	20 †
0-6-0	1923	-	3 *

Notes: * For NCC, 5 ft 3 in. gauge, to designs of Bowman Malcolm, CME of the railway.
        † For use on the LTSR section of LMS.

Appendix Five

Preserved Fowler Locomotives

Class	Type	No.	Built Date	by	Location
'4F'	0-6-0	43924	1921	Derby	Worth Valley
'4F'	0-6-0	44027	1924	Derby	Butterley
'4F'	0-6-0	44123	1925	Crewe	Avon Valley Rly
'4F'	0-6-0	44422	1927	Derby	North Staffs Rly
'7F'	2-8-0	53808	1925	Stephenson	West Somerset Railway
'7F'	2-8-0	53809	1925	Stephenson	Butterley
'2F'	0-6-0T	47279	1924	Vulcan Foundry	Worth Valley
'2F'	0-6-0T	47298	1924	Hunslet	Llangollen Railway
'2F'	0-6-0T	47324	1926	North British	Avon Valley Railway
'2F'	0-6-0T	47327	1926	North British	Butterley
'2F'	0-6-0T	47357	1926	North British	Butterley
'2F'	0-6-0T	47383	1926	Vulcan Foundry	East Somerset Railway
'2F'	0-6-0T	47406	1926	Vulcan Foundry	Peak Railway
'5P5F'	2-6-0	42700	1926	Horwich	National Railway Museum, York
'5P5F'	2-6-0	42765	1927	Crewe	Worth Valley Railway
'5P5F'	2-6-0	42859	1930	Crewe	Hull Dairycotes
'6P'	4-6-0	46100*	1927	North British	Bressingham Museum
'6P'	4-6-0	46115*	1927	North British	Tyseley Museum

Note: * Preserved as rebuilt by Stanier.

Numbers given are those at withdrawal from BR stock.

Locomotive project studies
under Fowler

Date	Type	Ordered	Comments
1910	2-6-0	No	Project study for 4F
1911-12	2-10-0T } 2-6-6-2T } 0-6-6-0T }	No	Lickey banker studies
1920	2-8-0	No	Improved S&DJR type
1920	2-6-0	No	Shortened S&D 2-8-0
1924	4-6-0	No	3-cyl compound
1926	4-6-2	Yes	4-cyl compound Cancelled (Ch 7 & 8)
1926	2-8-2	No	4-cyl compound
1927	2-4-0T	No	Study for auto-train (water-tube boiler)
1928	0-6-2T	Yes	Cancelled in favour of 2-6-2T
1930	0-8-4T	No	Cylinders 20¾ in. x2 6 in., 200 psi boiler
1931	0-4-4T	Yes	Fowler probably had little to do with this, as he moved to research this year.

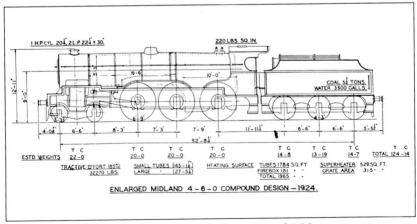

Fowler study for 3-cylinder compound 4-6-0.

Appendix Seven

The Paget Locomotive

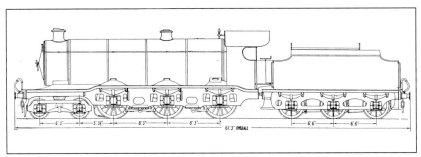

The Paget locomotive, the 4-6-0 that was not built.

It may not be generally known that the Paget design went through two distinct phases before it was settled that the second design would be the one to build. The first design study was for a 4-6-0 with four inside cylinders. One particular distinguishing feature for this locomotive was the lack of external coupling rods. The driving axles were coupled together by a complex arrangement of split rods near the centreline (in plan) of the locomotive. The cylinders were single acting and steam to them was admitted by rather complex ports cut in a rotary valve mounted on a vertical axis. Access to the motion appeared to be a nightmare and any maintenance tasks would clearly have been very difficult.

The boiler and firebox assembly was most unorthodox in that the firebox, well over 10 ft in length, was of a circular, corrugated, pattern very similar in concept to the L&YR 0-8-0 of Hoy employing this type of firebox. Whilst Hoy's design got to service on a batch of 20 built in 1903, they soon began to show problems, particularly in raising steam. This was occasioned by poor circulation which meant firing up the previous evening for the next morning's work. Quite probably this first design of Paget's, had it been built, would have suffered the same problem.

A drawing still exists and examination of this has produced the above analysis. However, this 4-6-0 design was scrapped in favour of the 2-6-2 that emerged from the second iteration study.

The Paget locomotive, as built. *JSM Collection*

Bibliography

A Historical Summary of the Royal Aircraft Factory and its Antecedents 1878-1918 - Report No. Aero 2150 by S. Child & C.F. Caunter.
A History of England by K. Feiling, Book Club Associates.
A History of the LMS by O.S. Nock, George Allen & Unwin.
ARLE Minutes (notes on) - compiled by Geoffrey Hughes.
British Locomotives of the 20th Century by O.S. Nock, PSL.
Crewe Locomotive Works by Brian Reed, David & Charles.
Derbians of Distinction by M. Craven.
Derby Works and Midland Locomotives by J.B. Radford, Ian Allan.
Derby and the Midland Railway by Peter Billson, Breedon Books.
Derby Daily Telegraph - various issues.
Derby Trader - 19th June, 1983.
Derbyshire Advertiser - 24th November, 1961.
Farnborough, the Story of RAE by R. Turnill & A. Reed.
Fowler Locomotives by Brian Haresnape, Ian Allan.
Historic Railway Disasters by O.S. Nock, 4th edition, BCA.
Lady Emma Fowler - Diaries.
LMS150 by P.B. Whitehouse and David St John Thomas, David & Charles.
Master Builders of Steam by H.A.V. Bulleid, Ian Allan.
Proceedings of the Institution of Civil Engineers.
Proceedings of the Institution of Mechanical Engineers.
Red for Danger by L.T.C. Rolt, David & Charles.
Richard Maunsell, An Engineering Biography by J.E. Chacksfield, Oakwood Press.
Sir Henry Fowler - Letters to Lady Fowler and his Bible class.
Spondon, A History by S. Watson.
The Aeroplanes of the Royal Aircraft Factory by Paul Hare, Crowood Press.
The Aspinall Era by H.A.V. Bulleid, Ian Allan.
The Four Great Railways by Michael R. Bonavia, David & Charles.
The Fowler Family by Robert Fowler & Jean E. Fowler, W. Lewis & Son, Herald Office, Bath.
The Lancashire & Yorkshire Railway by John Marshall, David & Charles.
The LMS Pacifics by J.W.P. Rowledge, David & Charles.
'The LMSR 9500 Class 0-8-0' by E.A. Langridge, *Stephenson Locomotive Society Journal.*
The Midland Railway by Roy Williams, David & Charles.
The Royal Aircraft Factory by Paul Harp, Putnam.
The Somerset and Dorset Railway by Robin Atthill, David and Charles.
'Under 10 CMEs' by E.A. Langridge, *Stephenson Locomotive Society Journal.*

Index

References to illustrations are shown in **Bold**.